Hidden:
The Unsolved Mystery of Sarah Mumford

HIDDEN

The Unsolved Mystery of Sarah Mumford

MICHELLE GRAFF

Cultivating Human Resiliency, Kansas City, MO

ISBN-13 (print): 978-1-7358817-3-7
ISBN-13 (e-book): 978-1-7358817-2-0

Library of Congress Control Number: 2023916527

Editor: Carol Trow
Cover: "Sarah Mumford" *The Niagara Sun,* July 25, 1899

When are cases too cold to be solved?
When is justice too old to be served?
When are lives lived too long ago to be remembered?

This book is for Amelia and Sarah and all the hidden girls.

Preface

In an old cemetery just outside of Pendleton, New York, a tombstone marks the grave of Sarah Mumford. The cleaned stone sits in a bed of white gravel. Flowers and porcelain angels adorn the grave. A caring person keeps it that way. The mystery of Sarah Mumford still captivates locals more than 120 years after her death. Though no one who lived when it happened is alive today, Sarah's story is still recalled by history buffs across Niagara County. The quest to find her justice is still alive.

I stumbled across Sarah's story on a different quest. My father never knew the names of his grandparents on his mother's side. This seemed odd to me since my grandmother was born less than ten miles from where I grew up in Niagara County. Armed with only a little information, I began a search for the truth. Along the way, I discovered the unsolved mystery of Sarah Mumford's death. Besides living in the same town at the same time, I noticed other parallels between Sarah's and my great-grandmother Amelia's stories. I was hooked. What started as family research became a mission to solve an extremely cold case.

The more I uncovered, the more I became compelled to solve both mysteries. With each discovery, the two stories became more entwined. I unearthed some startling revelations. And I realized that it was a story that needed to be told.

I decided to tell the two stories along the same timeline with alternating chapters. I wrote Sarah's story as narrative nonfiction. All the people, dates, events, and descriptions came from my research. Any dialogue came from direct quotes found in newspaper articles or historical records. I wanted readers to experience the events in the investigation as they happened so they could try to solve the mystery for themselves.

I wrote Amelia's story as historical fiction. The people, dates, and significant events were real. I created the dialogue. I wanted to give at least one of the girls a voice. Amelia's perspective was informed by my research of her life as well as documented accounts of what Pendleton residents thought about the murder. I took care not to create anything in the dialogue that would change the facts of Sarah's case.

What happened to Sarah and Amelia provides a glimpse into a darker time with societal issues still relevant today. It is also a mystery to be unraveled.

1
June 8, 1899

Engineer Roger Metcalf prepared the locomotive for departure, unaware that a week later he would be called to testify about the evening's events. Buffalo's New York Central Railroad station bustled with chatty theatergoers awaiting the train to carry them back to Lockport. Floral and feathered hats bobbed above the crowd as women jostled for one more chance to parade their evening attire. Chilled by the evening air, those in short sleeves pulled their shawls over their shoulders.

The Theater train, as it was known, took no more than forty-five minutes to transport passengers from the City of Lockport to Buffalo for an evening of amusement. The New York Central added it as a regular route in January of 1898 after railway officials received hundreds of requests from prominent members of Lockport society. The non-stop train proved popular. Members of Lockport social circles reveled in the privilege of riding the train into Buffalo to attend theatrical performances.

Conductor Harry Conway, dressed in his brass-buttoned uniform, signaled to the crowd to board the train. He checked for tickets as they settled in their seats. The din of chatter filled the car with recaps of the evening's best lines and occasional outbursts of laughter.

That night, all three of the major Buffalo theaters had performed comedies, adding an extra lilt to the always lively crowd. The Lyceum Theatre treated their audience to *The Geisha*. The well-known opera offered a light-hearted look at the stories and tribulations of indentured women.

The train left the downtown station at half past eleven. The lateness of the hour began to show on the faces of some of the passengers.

Before midnight, the train neared the town of Pendleton. Most Thursday evenings, the small farming community would have been tucked away sleeping long before that hour. Engineer Metcalf and his fireman Frank Turner sat in the cab looking out of the front window. Inside the train, the passengers softened their voices. Some battled sleepiness, some still chatted about the play, but no one heard the commotion outside as the train rumbled past Mapleton station. At midnight the Theater train passed Shawnee crossing right on schedule.

About a quarter of a mile up the track, engineer Metcalf noticed something wrong with the air brake on his train. He brought the engine to a halt and climbed down to locate the problem. He discovered a plug had been knocked off from the brake pipe near the bottom of the engine. It looked like the train had struck an obstacle, but after a quick check, he found nothing else concerning. He fitted a wooden plug into the valve and continued toward Lockport.

They rolled into Lockport station at almost a quarter past midnight. Passengers took little notice of any disruption as they departed the train and returned to their comfortable homes.

It was not until the next morning, when Metcalf performed a closer examination of the locomotive, that he made a startling discovery.

1895

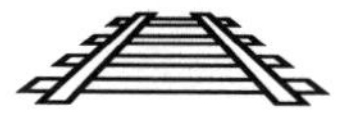

2
Sarah's Story
April 22, 1895

"A girl must be roused by having the soul in her recognized, her individuality recognized, her 'self' recognized as of real importance to somebody outside herself. Her little trials as well as her great ones must be weighed & considered. She must not be put down but lifted up till the facts of life can be brought before her in their true bearings."

—Elizabeth Cabot Putnam, Child Welfare Pioneer, 1897

Mondays began the drudgery that marked life in an orphanage. But that day—the 238th day of her most recent residency in the Rochester Orphan Asylum—Sarah Mumford might have sensed something would be different. The 11-year-old girl, with dark eyes and brown hair, sat on the small wooden chair next to her assigned cot. A neat row of snowy white iron beds, with white sheets and pillow shams, lined either side of the dormitory. On her lap, Sarah held a small wash basin containing a toothbrush, comb, and washrag. She waited for her group's turn in the lavatory.

Nearly 150 children inhabited the Rochester Orphan Asylum. The institution's two-winged structure had been erected in 1844 for the sole purpose of saving orphaned children from lives of destitution and debauchery, all thanks to the efforts of a group of benevolent women who had seen a need and took it upon themselves to respond.

In the first half of the nineteenth century, the construction of the Erie Canal had created boomtowns in its path. The town of Rochester exploded into a city. But along with wealth, the canal brought migrant workers and immigrant families. The sprawling dockside communities changed both the physical and social structure of Rochester. They also created a growing population of indigent children, posing a problem for concerned and upright citizens. Building an orphanage seemed like the ideal solution. The orphans traded a life of uncertainty for a life of regimen.

But orphan life posed a new set of problems that the benevolent women had not anticipated. Caring for many children in one setting on a limited budget proved difficult. Keeping the 'saved' children healthy and free from disease was a costly uphill struggle.

Orphanages like the one in Rochester recognized the need to place children out of the institution to manage their limited budgets. However, finding good homes for children was difficult and time-consuming. The practice emerged of indenturing children to families or workhouses. The orphans received food, shelter, and useful trade skills–including domestic duties for girls–in exchange for their labor. Indenturing children was an accepted practice supported by New York State statutes, and by mid-century, it became the fate of most orphans placed at the Rochester Orphan Asylum.

For the orphans remaining in the institutions, managing their behavior was another problem. Matrons intentionally designed a structure of discipline and regimen to keep their wards under control. Strict order, reinforced by threats of punishment, was initially believed to help prepare children for life outside the asylum. It usually had the opposite effect. Children became 'institutionalized'–the term used to describe the behaviors of one unable to think and act independently or successfully function outside an institution. Nonetheless, conformity had become a way of life in most orphanages, including the one that contained Sarah Mumford.

Sarah dressed in a uniform gray frock with a white pinafore. She lined up with the other children to go to the dining hall for their morning meal. The children descended a wooden staircase and filed down the long corridor. An endless row of windows stretched to the ceiling. They passed other groups of marching children in similar attire. Perhaps Sarah studied their faces in search of her older sisters.

Sarah had not seen her sister Kittie since Christmas. On the previous Christmas Day, the dining hall had displayed an abundance of donated cake, fruit, and candy with relaxed rules of how much could be eaten. To children in orphanages, holidays seemed like bright bursts of color on a canvas of gray. Sarah and Kittie experienced it together. Their oldest sister Grace had been sent elsewhere because she was deemed too old and unruly to be contained in the Orphan Asylum. The day after Christmas, Sarah searched in vain for Kittie. But she, too, had been taken away.

By the late 1880s, the Rochester asylum resorted to indentured servitude arrangements only in cases of older or unplaceable inmates. But they still struggled to manage the children in their care. In 1889, The New York State Board of Charities launched a formal investigation after receiving several complaints from former employees. The charges included, among other things, excessive whipping of the children, holding them under water, and punishing children who wet the bed by placing the urine-soaked sheet over their heads. The matron at the time told the investigator that she 'has to whip a great deal.' The hearing devoted a lot of time debating the size of the whip used.

The investigation also revealed only a twenty-five percent infant mortality rate, well below average for bottle-fed babies who lacked the natural immunity provided by mother's milk. The investigator commended the institute for their efforts in health and sanitation. He acknowledged the inherent difficulty of controlling so many children. In his final report, he did not recommend the elimination of corporal punishment but rather that discipline measures be regulated by guidelines, documentation, and oversight. The board of managers accepted the recommendation and promptly dismissed the matron. It was not until 1895 that the Rochester Orphan Asylum decided to ban corporal punishment. Although 'sparing the rod' was still considered progressive, the board of managers likely desired to avoid further scandal.

The new matron had brought a sense of order to the asylum. The children helped keep the floors and staircases scrubbed. The smell of turpentine and linseed oil permeated the corridor. While death and disease plagued most orphanages, the Rochester asylum had not recorded a fatality in over eighteen months.

Had her day not been interrupted, Sarah would have spent much of it in the school room receiving lessons, followed by a routine of domestic chores including cleaning and sewing. The inmates made, at least in part, many of the garments and linens used at the asylum. But that day, Matron Dinehart summoned Sarah for a reason the child likely did not know.

Sarah followed behind the matron back down the long corridor. They walked past the two large playrooms used on days when the matron deemed the weather too miserable to go outside. Sarah likely missed many a play hour, the fate of children who struggled to follow the rules. She might have preferred the drop of quinine on the tongue. The bitter taste lingered, but it proved less of a deterrent for some children than others. Neither punishment seemed to be as effective as making a naughty boy dress in one of the girl's frocks. Matron Dinehart had exercised some creativity since the board of managers banned corporal punishment.

The matron attributed Sarah and her sisters' difficulties to their experience before the asylum. "The early life of these children was such to make them cold and rough. We fear that they will not be kept long in any good home," she wrote in their file after they were returned from a placement the previous September.

When Sarah and Miss Dinehart arrived at the office, a man dressed in a waistcoat and jacket stood at the door. It was unknown if Sarah protested, though it would have done her no good. Children rarely had a voice in the decisions made for them. Matron Dinehart instructed her to go with the man. Eleven-year-old Sarah did not know if she would return to the orphanage or ever see her sisters again.

3
Amelia
May 14, 1895

Inside a wood-framed house on Bear Ridge Road in the town of Pendleton, New York, 13-year-old Amelia Knople, the youngest and soon-to-be only child in her family, moved with a nervous helplessness. A gingham kerchief covered her twin braids of light brown hair. Her soft blue eyes welled with tears, as she tried to bring her mother and ailing sister whatever they needed.

Amelia's parents, Henry and Ricca Knople, were subsistence farmers, producing not much more than they needed to survive and some years a little less. Amelia's father—like his father—believed land ownership was key to prosperity and would hang on to it at all costs. Ricca—who had learned to read and write English as a young girl—believed education could lift them out of poverty. But both placed their hope in their children—the first generation of Americans who would change the course for their family.

Ricca sat near the bed of her dying child, something she had done four times before. The first time had been more than a quarter century earlier when she lost Laura, a sister Amelia knew only by name. Three more children, a boy, and two girls, made it to young adulthood before death had taken them.

Ricca held a water-soaked rag to her daughter's lips. "Drink, Rachael," she whispered. Her gray-streaked hair pulled away from her face, exposing her tired eyes. She turned toward Amelia. "Where's your father? He should be back by now." Amelia had no answer. Her father had gone to ask her uncle, who lived on the property, to fetch the doctor.

Amelia heard the kitchen door open. A moment later her father came into the room. He was still dressed in his work clothes and held a straw-brimmed hat.

"Doctor's right behind me," he said. "Had to go all the way to Martinsville." Sorrow strained his ruddy face.

"Why didn't you send Fritz?" Ricca asked.

"He wasn't in a good way," he answered. Amelia knew that meant her uncle was drunk. Her mother asked no more questions.

When the doctor arrived, he was not the old physician who had attended to her family before. This doctor looked to be not much more than thirty. A beige tweed suit with a long jacket covered his tall frame. Beneath his spectacles, he directed his gaze at Amelia's parents when he spoke.

"I'm Doctor Helwig." The doctor took off his hat and set his brown medicine bag on the bedside table. He placed his hand on Rachael's forehead.

"The family she works for brought her home this morning because she fainted," Ricca said. Rachael worked as a domestic for a family with the means to hire a live-in servant.

"How long has she been sick?" Dr. Helwig asked.

"She seemed fine when she left Sunday night," Ricca said, "but thirsty. She's been that way for weeks."

Dr. Helwig slid a chair next to the bed. Amelia's sister lay still beneath his hands. "Her skin is parched. She's lacking fluid."

"I've been trying to get her to drink, but she won't stay awake long enough to take water," Ricca said. She stared at the doctor as he placed his stethoscope on Racheal's heart. Her chest no longer rose and fell.

Amelia spoke up. "She was afraid the mistress would get angry if she excused herself too often." The doctor looked at Amelia. She could see the pity in his eyes.

Dr. Helwig turned back to Ricca. "You did the right thing," he assured her. "But I'm afraid it's too late." He slowly folded his stethoscope and placed it back in the bag. "I'm sorry." Dr. Helwig rose to his feet.

Amelia felt her stomach quiver as she realized what the doctor was saying. Warm tears spilled from her eyes. Her father went to her mother's side and placed his heavy hands on her shoulders.

Ricca stood and faced the doctor squarely.

"We have no money to pay you today," she said. The quiver in her voice was barely detectable. "We lost another daughter just this past year and we still owe the undertaker."

Helwig looked at his surroundings and shook his head.

"I'm afraid I was not of much service," he said. "If you're concerned about the burial costs, there are provisions for the poor that... "

At the word poor, Amelia's father turned away. She could feel her own body stiffen at the sight of her father's embarrassment.

Dr. Helwig tried a different approach. "My parents are from Germany, too. I grew up nearby in Clarence," he said. Amelia's mother stared at the doctor as if she was deciding whether to believe him or not.

"If you let me make some arrangements," Helwig continued, "I can see to it she gets a proper burial at the city cemetery." Ricca and Henry glanced at each other but neither responded.

"You're Lutheran?" Dr. Helwig asked.

"Methodist," Ricca said. "Just up the road."

"I'll contact the pastor to make the arrangements," the doctor offered.

Neither of Amelia's parents had the energy to protest.

When the doctor left, the three sat quietly. An oil lamp provided a dim light in a room otherwise darkened by death. Both Amelia and her father watched Ricca closely as if she were the gatekeeper for the family's grief.

"I need to write to Philip," Ricca finally said. Amelia wondered where her mother would send the letter. The Knoples' only remaining son had left home to find work in the city. The family had still not heard from him.

Ricca rested her head in her hands "What will we do?" she said softly. It was not the time to speak of money, but some of Rachael's pay had helped to support the family. Amelia understood her mother's need to focus on something she could control.

"When Fritz's pension is reinstated, he will help," her father said.

"*If* his pension is reinstated." Ricca sighed. "Since they took it away, he's only gotten worse."

"He's in pain, the war injury—"

Ricca held up her hand to stop him. Her husband's unwavering defense of his older brother was something Amelia's mother seldom bothered to challenge. But today she did not want to hear it. Amelia's Uncle Fritz had broken his ankle fighting in the Civil War. After nine months in an army hospital treated with morphine, he came home with a noticeable limp and a powerful addiction.

Ricca looked at her husband. The years of toil and loss stretched across his brow.

"Heard Mr. Tripp might be looking for a girl." He spoke softly. "Amelia's almost fourteen."

"Nein," Ricca responded without giving the idea any consideration. "I will not let another child leave my home to serve someone else's family," Ricca spoke this part in German. Her parents did this so often to keep things from her that Amelia had become quite good at understanding the language.

"Annie was no older when she left to work," her father said.

"And if I could change that decision, I would." Ricca stopped abruptly. A dark silence hung between Amelia's parents.

Ricca lowered her head and then looked over at Amelia. She stared at the child as if she was considering her entire life. Slowly, she began to shake her head from side to side. "Children belong with family," she said. "Amelia will stay in school."

No more was spoken of it. Amelia's father also knew when not to challenge his wife.

1899

4
Sarah's Story
June 8, 1899

Six-year-old Flora Thompson opened her eyes and looked at the ceiling. She heard a loud knock on the front door. The night still darkened her room.

Someone knocked again, a bit louder this time. She heard the door open and the sound of her father's voice. The curious girl slipped from her bed and listened by the stair door. The voices sounded familiar. She recognized her father's voice and that of their neighbor, Mr. Tripp.

Henry Tripp and his son Lauren pleaded with her father to help search for their missing girl. Flora could not hear all they were saying, but she sensed the urgency in their voices.

Maybe Sarah ran away, Flora later recalled thinking.

Burt Thompson, Flora's father, was the postmaster at Mapleton Station. The station and post office, a one-room schoolhouse, and a small Presbyterian church surrounded by wooded patches, newly planted fields, and a dozen or so farmhouses, made up the tiny village of Mapleton in the northwest corner of the town of Pendleton, New York. A small stream known as Bull Creek ran somewhat parallel to the train tracks that cut through the village.

Henry Tripp and his son Lauren had begun knocking on doors about 10:00 p.m. that evening looking for Sarah, the Tripp's 16-year-old 'adopted' daughter. They told neighbors she had left the house at about 9:00 p.m. without saying where she was going. Henry Tripp added that she was not wearing her bonnet, a detail that would be repeated many times. When she had not returned home by the end of the hour, he relayed, he and his wife became worried.

None of the neighbors reported seeing her at all that evening. A few men, led by the Tripps, initiated a search of the area. By this time darkness had settled in.

In a village as small as Mapleton, people knew their neighbors' comings and goings well. They all knew who Sarah was, they had seen the brown-haired girl before, though not recently.

The searchers combed the woods and the banks of the creek. They checked the cemetery where Sarah liked to go. The Theater train rumbled past Mapleton station. The sound of the weekly train would have marked the time for anyone still searching. It was almost midnight. The girl remained unlocated.

When Henry and Lauren Tripp returned from the search, they deliberated what to do next. Sometime after 1:00 a.m. Henry Tripp hitched up his light buggy and headed to the nearby city of Lockport. He drove more than six miles to the police station to notify the authorities. At 2:00 a.m. the Lockport police took down the report. Mr. Tripp relayed the same facts he had told his neighbors. His young ward, Sarah Mumford, had left the house without her bonnet at 9:00 p.m. When she had not returned by 10:00, they began searching the neighboring area. When they had not been able to locate Sarah, he decided to report her missing to the authorities.

The police promised to make a sweep of the Lockport establishments, in case she had come into town. But no one had seen the missing girl

5
Amelia

Amelia lay awake in her bed. Something had startled her sleep. Was it something she heard? She rolled to her side hoping to get comfortable. A moment later she returned to her back.

Then she heard it again, the sound of muffled shouts somewhere in the distance.

A few minutes later she heard her father rise from his bed, with the low grunt he always emitted when standing to his feet. When she heard him in the kitchen, she decided to join him. Amelia sat up and swung her feet to the floor. She paused for a breath and wondered if she could still stand without grunting like her father. She was only seventeen, but as her condition progressed, she sometimes felt as old as her parents.

"What is it?" she whispered, as she entered the kitchen.

"What is what?" He lit the lantern, illuminating his rugged face. Her father quickly shifted his eyes away from her. "Why are you up?"

"I heard noises outside. People noises, sounded like it was coming from the fields."

Henry Knople tilted his head to one side to listen. His hearing had been gradually failing since Amelia was a small child. He slowly shook his head back and forth.

"Go to bed, Amelia," he said. "It is still the middle of the night."

She thought to ask him why he was awake but stopped. She knew he started the habit of waking up to worry, ever since he had learned of her condition.

Amelia stood silently and then turned back to her room. She stopped to peer out the window across the darkened fields before crawling back to bed. Whatever caused the noise had stopped. Maybe she had imagined it. Amelia's parents were her only contact with the outside world, and her father barely raised his eyes to look at her. Her life had become so isolated that perhaps she was hearing voices to fill the void.

It was just Amelia and her parents since her uncle had gone to the veteran's home. A welcomed peace had settled in the house when Uncle Fritz first left three years prior. Her uncle was often in a bad way, as her father called it when his older brother got tanked up. His addiction had cost him his war pension. But as time went on, the United States government recognized the need to care for their wounded soldiers—including the hundreds of thousands struggling with addictions. Pension laws eased, and Uncle Fritz had his pension reinstated. He took refuge at the National Home for Volunteer Soldiers in Dayton, Ohio. Uncle Fritz received treatment for his pain but was taken far from his family. Now the house felt so empty, and Amelia felt so restless, that she longed to be entertained by one of his stories.

Amelia eased back into bed and tried to find a comfortable position. She closed her eyes and hoped for sleep. It had been more than a month since she had fallen into deep rest. Amelia did not know if her insomnia was caused by the discomfort of her condition or the fear of what was to come.

6
Sarah's Story
June 9, 1899

In the early hours of Friday morning, 19-year-old Charles Bliss followed his usual route on his way to work. The dirt road stretched along flat, like many in Niagara County. The sun had already breached the horizon as he passed the Comstock farm heading east towards Lockport. When he neared the tracks of the New York Central Railroad, a golden blanket of light spread across the road. Bliss noticed something scattered on the far side of the track.

A thick row of brush and trees lined the crossing. As he drew closer, he squinted to see what now appeared to be mangled human remains. When he neared the body, he could tell by a calico skirt it was a young woman. Torn pieces of gingham fabric covered the torso. It looked as though the train had dragged her some distance. The wheels had severed her legs, and one side of her face was badly crushed. One of her hands still stretched across the rail.

Bliss notified the neighbors. Someone summoned the coroner.

Niagara County–located in the westernmost part of New York State–was bordered on three sides by water: Lake Ontario to the north, the Niagara River to the west, and the Erie Canal to the south. The mostly rural county was divided into twelve 'towns' forming a rough grid. The body had been discovered in the town of Cambria, directly north of the town of Pendleton where the Tripp family lived.

Henry Cleveland, the Niagara County Coroner, resided in the city of Lockport, the county seat. A 43-year-old bachelor, Cleveland lived by himself in a small house on Waterman Street. Even if he had been awake and dressed, it would have been at least thirty minutes before he arrived to view the scene.

Cleveland had twice been elected as coroner of Niagara County. The first time was in 1892. He served for four years, earning a reputation as a dedicated civil servant. He regained the job in the 1898 election by a hefty margin despite an otherwise lackluster showing by his fellow democrats. The role did not require a medical background. It was largely a political position held by loyal party members, and Cleveland was a loyal Democrat. He was also a dentist by trade, and he took his position as coroner quite seriously.

When he had received the report that morning that the body of a young girl had been found on the rails, he knew to expect an unpleasant scene. To be 'killed by cars,' as death by train was often referred to, was an unfortunate but common fate in the late nineteenth century. This would be the fifth train fatality that Cleveland had responded to since the beginning of the year. It was his job as coroner to determine if it was by accident or suicide.

Though Cleveland had seen his share of train deaths, it was always worse when it involved a child. Just a little over a month prior, he had been called to the scene of a gruesome accident at a train crossing in Lockport. A 16-year-old girl had stepped in front of a New York Central train near Hawley Street. The impact threw the young girl nearly twenty-five feet. Witnesses stated that she meant to cross and misjudged the speed of the train. After viewing the remains and interviewing bystanders, he ruled it an accident.

By the time Cleveland arrived at Shawnee crossing, Engineer Metcalf would have already made his gruesome discovery and alerted his superiors that someone had been struck on the theater run somewhere before Lockport Junction. The railway agent from Lockport was dispatched to the site of the accident.

Cleveland scanned the tracks and their surroundings. Heavy brush spilled from the tree line and, perhaps, had obstructed the view of the engineer. It seemed evident that the girl had been struck by the train, but he would wait for the railroad agents before having the body removed. In the meantime, he carefully studied the position of the remains. The body, most of it, lay on the east side of the planking near the track. Something struck Cleveland as peculiar.

Agent John Perhamus of the New York Central Railway arrived shortly to make his observation and provide what information he had to offer. As station agent, Perhamus was responsible for all trains coming in and out of Lockport. The last train to pass, the agent confirmed, was the Buffalo to Lockport Theater train that had crossed this point on time at 12:00 a.m. that morning. It would have been traveling at a speed well over thirty miles per hour.

This would have further perplexed Cleveland. Why would a young girl be out walking alone at that time of night?

The railway agent echoed his suspicion. But she was not walking, he attested. If she had been standing when the engine hit her, the impact would have thrown her away from the tracks. He speculated that she intentionally threw herself in front of the locomotive. Suicide was the railwayman's professional opinion.

Cleveland would not rush to judgment. His first task was to determine the identity of the young girl. He conducted a few short interviews of gathering neighbors from the nearby farms. They shared the story of the girl who had gone missing the night before. No one had seen her pass along the highway.

Coroner Cleveland ordered the body to be taken to the Prudden Brothers Undertaking in Lockport for examination. Sometime before four that afternoon, Henry Tripp confirmed that the mangled remains were his adopted daughter Sarah. Cleveland would have to have asked the delicate question. Mr. Tripp reported that he could not imagine why she would have any cause to commit suicide. He speculated that she left home and walked almost three miles to that stretch of track toward Lockport. He did not offer any reason why she would have run away. According to Henry Tripp, Sarah had been treated with nothing but kindness. She was considered one of the family.

The coroner gave some weight to Agent Perhamus' opinion. His theory that it must be suicide, based on the position of the remains, made sense. But Cleveland was not ready to come to a hasty conclusion one way or the other. Perhaps something else stuck out about the gruesome scene of Sarah's death. Or maybe the way the family responded to the death did not set well with Coroner Cleveland. Either way, it was his job to dig deeper when the circumstances warranted.

Cleveland impaneled a coroner's jury of eight men. He scheduled the inquest for two o'clock the following Thursday, June 15, at the Prudden Brother's Undertaking in Lockport.

7
Amelia

Amelia's feet hurt. She sat down and loosened her bootlaces but resisted the urge to pull them off completely, afraid they wouldn't fit back on. She had spent the better part of the afternoon finishing the ironing. It was getting harder each day to stand for so long. Amelia had tried to convince her mother that there was no sense in pressing her clothes because she never left the house. Ricca would not have it.

The back door stood open to let in the breeze. Amelia longed for the spring she was missing. Born in the town of Pendleton, Amelia had never been outside Niagara County. She dreamed of seeing the exotic places she read about in her books. But spring transformed her hometown into a world as beautiful as any. The land took on a lushness with as many shades of green as one could imagine. The proximity to Lake Ontario made the soil fertile and the air humid, perfect for growing fruit. Cool spring breezes carried the sweetness of wheat and apple blossoms. Niagara Falls was a mere thirty miles away. Amelia had never actually seen them, but just knowing the majestic wonder was nearby made her feel she lived somewhere special.

This year she had missed it all. She had been confined to their house for months and spent most days in the kitchen helping her mother with chores. The room felt small and cramped. A high wooden table lined the wall with bowls and tin canisters on top and large basins stacked beneath. A black iron stove with a flat top was attached to the adjacent wall with a wooden stool in the corner. Across from the stove stood a large dresser that Amelia's grandmother had painted green many years prior. The door on the far wall hung next to a row of hooks and led to the backyard. In the center sat a small wooden table with three chairs, the center of Amelia's world.

Her father came in through the back door, looking old and hungry. Amelia got up slowly to help her mother get the evening meal on the table. They ate late on Fridays. Her father had found work forking hay on a larger farm to bring in extra income. He left before sunrise and got home sometime after eight.

"Washed up?" Ricca asked.

"Before I came in," her husband answered. He hung up his hat and sat down. Ricca pushed his plate in front of him.

"They found someone on the rails this morning," he said between bites. "Killed by the night train. They think it was the young Tripp girl."

Ricca stiffened her brow. "She couldn't have been more than sixteen?" She looked at her daughter to see if she knew.

Amelia shrugged. "Don't know," she said. "I've heard Henry and Mary Burmeister talk about her. I think her name was Mary or maybe Sarah." She tried to remember what they called the girl. Henry and Mary were her mother's half-siblings. Amelia's grandmother had died when Amelia was an infant. Then her grandfather remarried a young widow named Catherine Bender, who already had a baby boy. Henry Bender was now Amelia's age; Mary Burmeister was three years younger.

"What was she doing out on the rails so late at night?" Ricca asked her husband.

Amelia's father continued to swallow another bite before he answered. "Told you all I know," he said. He quietly pushed a potato onto his fork.

Amelia tried to picture the girl who lived with the Tripp family. It had been more than a year since she had seen her, and they had never spoken. It was hard not to think about what she would look like after being struck by a locomotive. Amelia wondered if she felt the pain of her death. She placed her hands on her stomach. The thought of it made her queasy. Amelia knew death. She had witnessed it take the lives of four older siblings, none of them much older than she was now.

Ricca noticed her daughter's light skin turn peaked. "Sit, Amelia," she said. "You need to eat something."

Amelia sat, but she wasn't hungry. She felt the familiar darkness sweep through her, settling in the bottom of her gut. Amelia still longed for her departed siblings, including her brother Philip who had left home, never to be heard from again. She missed Rachael and the way they laughed and teased each other. She missed talking with her sister Mary about books they both read. She remembered Charles taking her fishing along the canal. But most of all, she missed Annie. Her oldest sister had died when Amelia was only six years old. Annie had helped her mother tend to Amelia so much that the two had formed a powerful bond. When consumption had slowly drained Annie of life, Amelia was left with a heavy hole in the pit of her chest.

She glanced over at her mother. Ricca sat silently watching her husband eat; her gray hair pulled back in a tight bun. Amelia searched for a hint of sorrow in her face. Her mother's display of grief never came close to matching what Amelia felt. But Amelia sensed it was there. She imagined that Ricca pushed her feelings down so far that they steadied her like an anchor. Ricca rarely lost her composure. But Amelia feared her mother's capacity to endure another loss was near its end.

8
Sarah's Story
June 11, 1899

The regional newspapers carried the story of Sarah Mumford's death, including Henry Tripp's account of her having gone missing the night before. Already, the press speculated that it might be a case of suicide. The *Auburn Bulletin* ran a piece on the front page of the four-p.m. edition the day Sarah's body was discovered. The bold type title read "Was it Suicide?" but the official death registration listed Sarah Mumford's death on June 9th and the cause simply as 'killed by cars'.

Journalists were not the only ones with opinions. Word of Sarah's death spread through the town of Pendleton. The farming community, perched on the Erie Canal and nestled between the cities of Lockport and North Tonawanda, had something more than the lack of rain to talk about. As the people of Pendleton heard of the tragedy, rumors emerged that young Sarah was in a delicate condition. The origin of this widely held opinion was unclear. Had someone witnessed a liaison? Had Sarah shared a secret with a confidant? Had neighbors seen the girl, who was reported as large for her age, and surmised that she was with child? Or, as some would say, did a member of the family first suggest the scandal? Either way, the story took hold and spread fast.

In 1899, an unmarried girl in a delicate condition faced degradation and shame. People speculated that this was enough to provoke a girl to take her life by throwing herself in front of a moving train.

Either a suicide or an unwed pregnancy posed a scandal for a reputable family like the Tripps. To have both asserted was hard to contain. The Tripps held a quiet funeral for their adopted daughter without placing a notice in the paper. The burial took place on Sunday, two days after her body was discovered. Since it had been assumed that the train caused her death, no autopsy was performed.

It was customary at the time. and with the Tripp family, to hold a service at the family home before proceeding to the gravesite. But Sarah would not have been fit for viewing. They buried her near their family plot in the Shawnee cemetery just a few miles from where her body was discovered. A few family members and neighbors gathered to pay their respects to the unfortunate girl.

Horace Chadsey might have led a graveside service; he was the pastor of the Presbyterian Church located less than a mile from the Tripp home. At one time, Sarah attended church and Sunday school and took a principal part in church festivals. She sang with a sweet voice according to those who heard her. Perhaps the pastor recalled her singing. Chadsey was more than just a minister. He was also one of Tripp's nearest neighbors.

The Tripp family was well known to the people of Niagara County. Mr. Tripp's father had been one of the first pioneers of Pendleton. Henry Tripp Sr. had settled on a large tract of land in 1824, three years before Pendleton was officially formed. They had already been well established long before German immigrants added to the town's population in the latter half of the century. The Tripp family prospered and as their family grew, so did their farmland. Henry Tripp Jr. was number three of ten children. His brother, Daniel, also owned a large farm in Pendleton. Henry's farm stretched more than 60 acres. His home, one of the largest in the area, reflected their prosperity.

Likely, not many of the extended Tripp family attended Sarah's funeral. But Henry Tripp stood solemnly over the open grave. The old farmer's dark suit hung on a slender frame; his bearded face tilted forward. The frail Matilda Tripp stood next to her husband of more than forty years. Behind them stood a headstone engraved in large letters with the name Egbert. The Tripp's oldest child had died at age seventeen, more than twenty years prior. His sudden death had been grieved not only by his family but his schoolmates in Mapleton.

Not far from her parents stood Henry and Matilda's middle child. Not yet married, Iva Tripp lived with her parents on the homestead. Her handsome features held some of her youth despite her twenties being four years behind her. She dressed in a simple black gown with full sleeves that underscored her trim figure. Iva was a schoolteacher but had not held a position for the past term.

Henry and Matilda Tripp's oldest living child, Addie, would also have attended the funeral. Addie had married into the Dersham family, a large clan that had migrated north from Pennsylvania a generation prior. Some settled in Niagara County; some went on to Michigan. Addie and her husband lived in Pendleton about five miles from her parents. The couple had given Henry and Matilda three grandchildren ages six, nine, and thirteen. But they were Dershams, not Tripps.

Lauren Tripp stood with his family next to the open grave of his adopted sister. He had the same dark hair and rounded features as his sister Iva, only on him it came across as boyishly good-looking. Lauren was Henry and Matilda's youngest and sole remaining son. He had been only four years old when his beloved older brother died.

Lauren had a wife. Addie had introduced Lauren to her unmarried sister-in-law, Carrie Dersham. The two had been married at Carrie's father's house in Michigan in 1896 before returning to Lauren's childhood home. They lived across the street from the Tripp family homestead in a small unpainted house. Not yet twenty-six, Lauren still worked on the farm with his father.

Mr. George Miller and his wife Lena arrived at the cemetery. The couple had two sons aged five and nine. Their farm sat near Tripp's property. The Millers had gotten to know Sarah over the years and had grown fond of the friendly child.

The Millers brought with them to the funeral their 17-year-old farmhand. Henry Bender looked more like an adolescent than a hired hand. His five-foot-six-inch frame had not yet filled out. Brown hair framed his round face and blue eyes. Henry grew up in Pendleton. He boarded with the Millers even though his own family lived not more than a couple miles away. He knew Sarah, the pretty girl who lived with the Tripps. Just how well was unknown. But Sarah had visited the Miller's farm where she found the sympathetic and willing ear of Mrs. Miller.

After the funeral service, a small meal might have been provided either in the ample sitting room of the Tripp home or the small Presbyterian church. Henry Tripp made it known that he had paid for the funeral himself, which amounted to no inconsiderable sum, according to the wealthy farmer.

Some who attended the funeral that day might have noticed Henry Bender talking to Mr. Tripp after the service. The young man standing close to the old farmer caught in conversation might have seemed odd. Onlookers might have also noticed that Mr. Tripp looked a bit uncomfortable.

9
Amelia

Amelia sat quietly with an open bible placed face down on her round belly. The house was empty. Her parents had not yet returned from Sunday service. She gently pressed her hand on the back of the bible as if she could push the words through her skin. She was supposed to be reading it. Her mother told her it was the proper thing to do if she could not go to church. Ricca had not allowed Amelia to attend services with the family since her condition had become more noticeable.

Amelia leaned her head back and closed her eyes. She tried to picture her parents standing outside the whitewashed church talking to friends. The mostly German congregation had provided a warm community for her family over the years. Amelia wondered if anyone noticed her absence. If they had inquired, Ricca would have hidden the truth. Sometimes, her mother acted as if she had contracted a terrible disease. Though she never asked who she had contracted it from.

The bible shook. Amelia set it on the side table and placed her hands softly over her belly. The baby kicked again. "I feel you," she whispered to the child growing in her womb.

The back door opened, and Amelia heard her parents come into the kitchen.

"...not proper to be speculating about the dead right there in the churchyard." Ricca was talking to her husband, but the conversation was one-sided.

"What's for dinner?" he asked.

"Yesterday's stew," Ricca answered, "just give me half an hour to warm it up."

Henry's face registered mild disappointment at Ricca's response. "Amelia could have started something while we were gone," he said.

"It was Amelia's time for worship, not work," Ricca said. "I'll make a cobbler for dessert."

Her husband, satisfied with that answer, left the kitchen.

Amelia got up to help her mother. She could tell by the set of her brow that she still had something left to say. Amelia hoped it was something interesting.

"People gossiping at church again?" she asked.

"Poor girl just laid to rest today and people are already passing stories." Ricca tied her apron around her waist.

"The Tripp girl?" Amelia asked. "What were they saying?"

"You know I don't share stories," Ricca said.

"I would've heard them if I'd been there."

Ricca looked at her daughter. "Sarah Mumford," she said. "If you're going to talk about her, you should use her proper name." She wiped her hands on her apron and turned to the counter. "People are saying it might not have been an accident that the train hit her, that she might have done it on purpose. Coroner's going to investigate." Ricca spoke the words as if they tasted bitter.

"Suicide?" Amelia said too loudly. The word made Ricca grimace. "Why would she take her own life?"

Ricca hesitated as if she was deciding whether to answer. "People are saying she was in a delicate condition." She paused again.

Amelia was not sure how to respond. She and her mother had hardly spoken about her own delicate condition. At least, not any more than necessary. "Oh," she finally said.

The two women finished preparing the meal. Nothing more was spoken about Sarah Mumford. But Amelia could not stop thinking about her for the rest of the day. She could picture Sarah now, not lifeless and mangled on the track, but alive with a round belly like her own.

Much of Amelia's seventeen-year life had been shadowed by death. She had been stricken with a loneliness that followed her everywhere and a numbness that robbed her of being fully present. But something changed when she realized she was pregnant. She was terrified, yes, but she was no longer alone. She moved her hands over her stomach. She could feel life not only growing in her womb but surging through her veins. Killing herself would mean taking her child's life, and it would be the last thing she would do.

Amelia felt sure that Sarah Mumford had not taken her own life.

10
Sarah's Story
June 15, 1899

Coroner Cleveland held the inquest at Prudden Brothers Undertaking on the evening of his forty-third and final birthday. Prudden Brothers occupied a four-story brick building in downtown Lockport. The structure, which once served as a multipurpose hall, contained the funeral establishment and a furniture store. The space proved a convenient location to hold an inquest with its spacious rooms and proximity to Cleveland's home and office.

Eight selected jurors gathered in the appointed room to hear the coroner present the evidence. This would be one of the last coroner's juries impaneled in Niagara County. A recently passed state law, set to go into effect September 1, 1899, abolished the practice. Critics believed that jurors were ill-equipped to understand the complexity of medical evidence. Since jurors usually went along with the opinion of the coroner, it was hard to justify the added expense. After September, the responsibility to determine the cause of death in an inquiry would fall to the coroner alone.

Jurors James Shaw, Edward Manning, George W. Pencille, Oliver Longmate, Frank A. Harmony, Charles P. Hemmer, Frank Watt, and James Nelson took their seats ready to perform their civic duty. Five were farmers from Cambria and likely knew the Tripp family. The other three lived in

Lockport: another farmer, a laborer, and a pump manufacturer. It was a task they likely thought would require no more than an evening or two of their time.

The inquest had attracted the attention of a few local reporters. Though train fatalities were common, the innuendos surrounding this case sparked a peculiar interest. Cleveland was bent on not muddling facts with rumors. He prepared to present a factual case to the jury panel.

Late nineteenth-century coroner inquests looked like any other court proceeding, except that the coroner ran the show. He chose what evidence to present and questioned the witnesses. There was no judge or defense attorney to confine him to the rules of evidence.

Most of the witnesses scheduled to testify before the panel were railroad officials and train hands of the New York Central Railroad. But there were many in attendance, and Cleveland wanted to hear from them all. The evidence, he believed, would lead them to the truth as to whether Sarah's death by train was an accident or self-inflicted.

But first, Henry and Matilda Tripp shared their account of the night Sarah went missing. Matilda was sworn in to give her testimony. Deep furrows across her forehead showed her age. Her nerves shook her voice as she described how she had last seen Sarah leave the house at about 9:00 p.m. She did not know where she was going. When she didn't return, the old woman said she went across the street to her son and daughter-in-law's house to see if Sarah was there, but neither had seen her.

Henry Tripp testified to the ensuing search and the decision to report her missing to the Lockport police when she was not found. He seemed to have accepted the theory that she had committed suicide but could give no reason why.

Cleveland likely asked more questions about who Sarah Mumford was and how she had come to live with the family. Henry Tripp told the jury how he had taken Sarah from the Rochester Orphan Asylum four years prior on April 22, when Sarah was twelve. They had given her a home and treated her like family, he was sure to add. His adopted daughter had retained her name, Sarah Mumford.

Cleveland shifted the focus to the railway workers. Railway employees knew a thing or two about what happened when a person was struck by a train. It happened regularly. At the time, death by train was the leading cause of accidental death in the United States. Steel locomotives ripped through rural communities at unprecedented speeds. Most crossings were unmarked. A hundred and fifty miles away in Chemung County, New York, their coroner investigated only fifteen deaths in the year 1899. Seven were killed by train cars.

Cleveland called the railmen to testify. Section boss James Donner gave his account of the accident scene on the morning of the 9th. He and his crew were charged with inspecting the tracks where the accident had occurred. Donner described the body mangled by the train but noted the lack of blood on the track or anywhere at the site. Two other trainmen on Donner's crew were asked to describe the scene; each noted the lack of blood on the tracks.

The jurors considered the expert opinion of Agent Perhamus. The position of the body indicated that Sarah had lain across the tracks. A body standing erect would have been thrown a distance from the tracks, the seasoned railwayman explained.

Robert Metcalf added his testimony. The train engineer told the jury that he had been the man at the helm the night of June

8th on the Buffalo-to-Lockport train. According to Metcalf, the train passed Shawnee crossing at midnight, its usual hour. Both he and his fireman were at the windshield watching the track. The engineer swore he saw or heard nothing. They did not even feel the train jar as it passed over the body. It was not until he noticed that the air brakes were not functioning properly that he realized something was wrong. Metcalf described how he stopped the train a quarter mile up the track to make his inspection. He could see that the train had struck something but did not know what. He testified that he examined the engine at that time, but when he found nothing, he continued to Lockport.

The engine, according to Metcalf, sat in the roundhouse overnight before making a morning run to Buffalo. At Blackrock station, he examined his engine again. This time he discovered a small piece of flesh, the size of a hen's egg yolk, on the front of the train. He reported his findings to the railroad officials.

Fireman Frank Turner testified next. He confirmed the engineer's story that they were both in their position at the window and saw nothing unusual.

The jurors also heard testimony describing the crossing as well shrouded by trees and brush. This and the darkness of the midnight hour would make spotting a still body, lying low on the track, difficult.

Harry Conway, the conductor on the theater train that night, testified to the train's schedule. He explained that the routine run transported theatergoers from Lockport to Buffalo early in the evening and back home again after the show. It leaves Buffalo at half past eleven, he told them. He confirmed that they left downtown Buffalo on time on June 8th. Anyone familiar with the tracks would know that the train passed through Mapleton right before midnight and Shawnee Crossing a few minutes later.

John Judge, a train wiper, also testified that he did not find any blood splatter when wiping down the engine or cars. But he did find a small bit of flesh on the cross beam of the cowcatcher.

By the end of the first session, the jury panel had heard several railmen note the absence of blood, an oddity that likely struck them as significant. The testimony seemed to be turning towards a ruling of suicide. But they were not yet ready to determine the manner of Sarah Mumford's death.

The inquest adjourned until the following week. Cleveland indicated that he needed to interview a few more witnesses to clarify some things.

Reporters from Lockport's *Niagara Sun* and the *Buffalo Times* urged the coroner to speculate on the colorful tales they had been hearing across town. Coroner Cleveland told the newsmen that he had not yet secured sufficient evidence to come to any conclusions. He refused to comment on any rumors without further investigation. Cleveland had his own method of sorting through facts to get at the truth.

The lack of blood reported by the trainmen hung in Cleveland's mind. He recognized it as important but determined not to jump to conclusions. The coroner remembered reading about something that might cause a body not to bleed in one of his books. He planned to research the point further. If solving the case required digging deeper, then deeper he would dig.

11
Amelia

June had been unusually hot and dry. Amelia found it hard to keep the sweat from dripping off her face and onto her mending. She was working on one of her father's shirts that had so many stitched-up holes and mismatched buttons that it looked like it belonged to a scarecrow.

Sarah Mumford had been stuck in Amelia's mind all week. She hoped the coroner would not make the mistake of thinking her death was a suicide just because she might have been in a delicate condition. But she knew too well that a young unmarried pregnant girl had very few options.

Girls like her were either turned out, to avoid the disgrace brought down on the family, or tucked away until another plan could be arranged. Maybe Sarah had been turned out by the Tripps and was walking to Lockport to find the father or seek shelter in the poorhouse. Amelia had considered doing the same. There was a time when the horrors of the county poorhouse seemed preferable to telling her parents and facing Ricca's wrath. But she knew that girls giving birth at the poorhouse had their babies snatched away just as soon as they were born and never saw them again. Amelia did not want her child to go to an orphanage. She heard they put infants in one big room and fed them dope to keep them from crying. Most of them died, she believed.

There were unspeakable ways a girl could take care of the situation herself. Amelia had heard that drinking oil of cedar would end a pregnancy. But she remembered a story about a girl who drank too much and died. Amelia had not given this option much thought.

When she finally got the nerve to tell Ricca, there was no wrath. Ricca, in step with her character, held her composure. She just went about things as usual, as if she had a plan. Only she never shared that plan with Amelia, and Amelia did not dare to ask. She was biding her time until the father made up his mind to provide for his child.

Amelia tied the knot on her seam and tore the thread in her teeth. She remembered hearing that Sarah had been an orphan before moving in with the Tripp family. She wished she had known her better. Amelia set the finished shirt to the side so that she could use both hands to stand. Her mother stood at the counter scrubbing a pot.

"Could I ask Mary Burmeister over on Sunday after church?" Amelia asked.

Ricca kept scrubbing. "What for?"

"For someone to talk to," Amelia said. She wanted to talk to someone who might know more about Sarah. "I haven't seen her since Henry's birthday. And that was four months ago." It was also just before her condition had begun to show.

"I don't think it's a good idea," Ricca said.

"Why not," Amelia said. "I could make a pie tomorrow. Mary would like that."

Ricca dried her hands on her apron and turned to face her daughter.

"I just don't think it's a good idea. Mary's only fourteen." Ricca said, looking at Amelia's ample belly. "And she looks up to you."

Amelia turned away from her mother, not able to face Ricca's scorn. She never asked for anyone to look up to her. Wasn't it enough that she carried the hopes and dreams of four dead sisters; and rather poorly at that. But Amelia understood what her mother was saying. Ricca had not told her younger half-sister about Amelia's condition. How long did her mother intend to hide her and the baby?

Amelia brushed a stray hair from her eyes. She had pulled her hair up that morning, but already her bun slid to the back of her neck. Loose curls now framed her face. She stared at her mother. Ricca's hair was smoothed back into a bun with any unruly strands tucked neatly out of sight. Everything for Ricca had a proper place. It was how she contained whatever injustice life dealt her family.

But Amelia's mother had failed to contain her unruly daughter. Amelia had never learned to be content with what she couldn't understand, and she just couldn't understand the unfairness of life. Why did good people die when their families needed them? Why were men given choices and women held accountable?

Suddenly, Amelia felt uneasy. She held the edge of the table to steady her balance. What if keeping her hidden was her mother's only plan? What happened when it was no longer possible? If the baby came before she heard from the father, where would she go?

12
Sarah's Story
June 16, 1899

Death created a disturbing, yet alluring diversion. It evoked people's darkest fears, prickled their curiosity, and drew them in with a morbid fascination. Edgar Allen Poe must have sensed this when he wrote *The Murder in the Rue Morgue* in 1841. More than fifty years later his dark tales remained a favorite source of entertainment. When *The Adventures of Sherlock Holmes* was published in 1892, Arthur Conan Doyle's books and fictional detective became widely popular in the United States. America, it seemed, loved a macabre mystery. Pendleton was no different.

Residents of the town began to share their theories as to what Sarah had been doing near the track that evening. Some argued that she had run away from home and the train struck her as she followed the track towards Lockport. Others believed strongly that Sarah was in a delicate condition, a predicament that left her with no other option but to throw herself in front of a train. Many offered even more sinister theories.

The rumors were not contained to the town borders. Within days of the discovery of Sarah's lifeless body, word reached the North Tonawanda police department that something was amiss. An unnamed North Tonawanda resident had visited Mapleton and heard ghastly stories that someone had caused Sarah's death. Police officials reported to the *Buffalo Evening Times* that they had received 'certain alleged facts' that warranted an investigation.

North Tonawanda had been incorporated as a full-fledged city just two years prior, a status that afforded the municipality a new police department with a chief, a sergeant, and six patrolmen. Eager as they were, this investigation was not in their jurisdiction. Until the coroner declared a crime had been committed, death was his domain. Instead, the North Tonawanda police put pressure on Coroner Cleveland by calling him out in the press as 'having a duty to perform'.

Cleveland accepted the challenge but refused to be rushed. Patience and persistence would mark his methodology; a lesson he learned early in life.

Henry Cleveland grew up in the town of Cambria, just North of Pendleton. The son of a blacksmith, his father died when he was only two. His mother was left to raise five children alone. Perhaps, she found single motherhood a struggle. She eventually remarried a farmer in the neighboring town of Porter. Henry, a good student, postponed his education to work on his stepfather's farm.

Cleveland later attended the Lockport Union School. The public school required serious students but charged no tuition. Because of his time off, he was much older than his classmates. But Cleveland found he excelled in mathematics, something that likely encouraged his goal to study medicine. He applied to the University of the City of New York; a school founded to provide affordable education to New York Residents.

But this too required patience. First, he took a job teaching in a small district school in the town of Porter. During his short tenure, he gained the affection of his students. At the close of the winter term of 1876, they presented him with a book of stories by Jonathan Swift, perhaps a nod to his love of reading.

Cleveland eventually left home to attend the University in New York City. He completed at least one year of their medical program in 1879. All this prepared him for his role as coroner.

It is possible Cleveland also read Arthur Conan Doyle's renowned books. Doyle based the character of Sherlock Holmes on a real-life physician he met while studying medicine at the University of Edinburgh. Dr. Joseph Bell's lectures on the power of observation and deduction inspired Doyle to fashion his great detective as a master in the art of forensics. Cleveland had developed a similar method of sifting through all the facts before theorizing, much like Sherlock Holmes. His comments to reporters reflected such.

Unfortunately, Cleveland found himself with many theories and not enough evidence. There was plenty of speculation by everyone within a ten-mile radius. Some stories emerged that the Tripps had used their adopted daughter as an indentured servant. None of it helped the coroner determine how Sarah had come to her demise. At least not yet. He concluded that he needed to consider each account and follow it to its origin.

For his part, Henry Tripp continued to paint the picture that Sarah lived an idyllic life. This might have also perplexed Cleveland. If it was true that all was well in the Tripp household, then why would Sarah run away or take her own life?

In a village as small as Mapleton, people knew their neighbors' comings and goings well, perhaps a bit more than those neighbors liked. To move the investigation forward he would have to interview those closest to the Tripps. He considered it an act of justice, not just for Sarah, but for the Tripp family as well.

Cleveland had less than a week before the inquest was scheduled to resume. Accompanied by a Pendleton resident, he began knocking on doors. Cleveland wrote down each name in case he needed to subpoena their testimony. With each interview, he listened carefully and recorded every detail. He asked questions to gain as much information as he could to paint the most accurate picture. What he would discover was something much darker than he had imagined.

13
Amelia

On Saturday, Aunt Katherine dropped in unexpectedly. As soon as she walked in the door her eyes darted right to Amelia's swollen belly.

"This is the reason you hide my niece from me, ja?" Aunt Katherine still spoke with a thick German accent, though, like Ricca, she had immigrated as a young girl. "I sensed there was trouble." She shook her head. Her silver hair wrapped around her crown and rested on top, like a bird's nest. Aunt Katherine had a direct manner that frequently turned people against her. But it was her most offensive qualities that Amelia liked the most. She never had to guess what her aunt was thinking.

"This is for you, Ricca," Aunt Katherine handed her sister-in-law a fistful of horseradish from her kitchen garden. She never came empty-handed. Aunt Katherine believed it was bad luck. "I have so much, and I know you like."

Actually, it was her brother-in-law who had a fondness for horseradish, but the two pretended not to like each other. Amelia believed the tension had something to do with Aunt Katherine leaving Uncle Fritz. People said she just got fed up with his drinking and temper. Amelia knew there was more to the story.

Aunt Katherine was Amelia's mother's oldest friend and Uncle Fritz's estranged wife. Ricca had been a witness at their wedding along with Fritz's younger brother Henry. A year later,

Ricca married Henry Knople and her friend became her sister-in-law. The two remained friends despite the turmoil of Aunt Katherine and Uncle Fritz's marriage.

Katherine turned to Amelia and placed her hands and her ear on Amelia's stomach. Then she nodded her head as if she heard something with which she agreed.

"Who is the father of this child?" The question stunned Amelia; even her mother had not yet asked. Before Amelia could think of a reply. Ricca interjected.

"Amelia is not ready yet to tell us," her mother said. "Come sit, I have fresh coffee."

Aunt Katherine sat at the table across from Ricca. Amelia sat on a stool in the corner, hoping the women would forget she was there. They spoke in German which made it a little harder to follow, but Amelia preferred it. They talked more freely in their native tongue as if they believed Amelia couldn't understand.

"How are the children?" Ricca asked.

"Fine, fine, my Freddie and Johnnie have both found good jobs."

"They are good boys," said Ricca. She pushed the sugar bowl toward her sister-in-law. "What is new in North Tonawanda?"

"What is new in North Tonawanda, you say? I should ask what is new in Pendleton." Katherine spooned the sugar into her cup. "This Mumford girl is all people want to talk about."

"Horrible accident," Ricca said.

"Ach, this was no accident," said Aunt Katherine. "This was foul play."

"Gossip," Ricca said.

"Nein, I sense it is so." Aunt Katherine sensed a lot of things.

"Why would anyone want to hurt the Tripp's adopted daughter?" Ricca asked.

"She was their adopted daughter, Ach." Aunt Katherine said. "She was unpaid labor, that is what she was to them."

Ricca did not respond.

"Spare the rod, ja, but I heard they beat her like no one should beat a dog." Aunt Katherine shook her head and sipped her coffee. "And she was in a delicate condition."

"That's all just rumors," Ricca said.

"Nein, this I heard came from someone who should know."

Amelia wanted to hear more of what she had to say, but she knew her mother would not entertain gossip. When Aunt Katherine did not get a response, she shifted the conversation.

"And what are you to do about this one?" Aunt Katherine asked with a slight nod toward Amelia as if the girl in the corner would not notice they were talking about her.

"What is there to do?" Amelia's mother responded.

"Ach, if you do not care about your own good name then at least think of the child." Aunt Katherine's tone harshened. "A baby born without a father will be marked as an outcast."

Ricca continued to drink her coffee.

"You are too old to pretend this one is yours." Aunt Katherine said to her friend.

Ricca looked at Amelia as if she was suddenly aware she was listening. "Tell me how little Henry is doing?"

"Not so little." Aunt Katherine smiled. "He is as tall as his brothers. He still likes school."

Amelia admired the way her mother could gently steer the conversation. Ricca's sensibilities were more subtle than

Katherine's, but Amelia knew they were there. Her mother was right about her not being ready to name the baby's father. When Amelia told him about the baby, the father asked her to keep his identity hidden until he decided what to do. So far, Amelia had stayed silent.

14
Sarah's Story
June 17, 1899

Cleveland might have been at odds with the press right from the start. They had different objectives. He was searching for facts, and they were looking for a good story. 1899 marked the height of yellow journalism—the practice of sensationalizing news events to boost sales as newspapers competed for readers. The style of hype and hyperbole over fact did more than sell papers, it shaped public opinion. When an explosion sank the U.S. Maine in 1898, newspapers had been fanning anti-Spain sentiment by publishing rumors of Spanish plots against U.S. ships. The *New York Journal* printed the unfounded headline in large capital letters: "Destruction of the War Ship Maine was the Work of an Enemy". Public outcry continuously flamed by the press pushed America into war with Spain.

Newspapers waged their own wars with rival papers. Even cities as small as Lockport—with a population of sixteen thousand at the time—had more than one newspaper. Papers pushed to scoop their competitor and capitalize on the public's fascination with death and scandal. As rumors about Sarah Mumford persisted, the newspapers began to run their version of the mystery.

Though pressed by the papers, Cleveland again refused to theorize. He told reporters that he needed to sift through all the evidence first. Perhaps he recalled the quote from Sherlock

Holmes: "It is a capital mistake to theorize before one has data. Insensibly one begins to twist facts to suit theories, instead of theories to suit facts." The coroner would feed the press no more than variations of that sentiment.

Cleveland was not the only one that the newsmen hounded for answers. A reporter from the *Buffalo Times* approached the schoolteacher who had taught Sarah at the Mapleton school. According to teacher Willis Hall, Sarah was a bright child. He did report that she displayed peculiar behaviors that might be difficult to manage.

"Did she strike you as the kind of girl who would run away and kill herself?" the newsman asked.

"She did not," he replied.

Hungry for more ways to sensationalize the story, journalists also pursued the Tripp family. They wanted Sarah's adopted family's reaction to the tragedy. Henry Tripp granted an interview to the *Buffalo Times.* He seized the chance to defend himself.

"I want to say that some people and some papers have published some nasty things about us. They are going to suffer for it. I want it understood that I and my family are as honorable as any in these parts." The elder Tripp felt the need to clarify that Sarah enjoyed a fine home life with his family since they had taken in the young girl four years prior.

"Sarah had often remarked that if it wasn't for us," Tripp said, "she should not know where to go for a home." He then offered more details of Sarah's last day. "My wife and daughter had been to the cemetery in the afternoon and took Sarah with them."

The cemetery, located on Mapleton Road, was a two-mile walk from the Tripp home. Sarah liked to visit the tree-speckled graveyard and frequently requested to go there. The Tripp women had their own reason for going to the cemetery. Egbert was buried there. His stone marked his grave in the family plot near the center of the lawn. Egbert's had been the first stone but not the only burial in the Tripp plot. A newer unmarked grave held the infant child of Lauren Tripp, lost only eighteen months prior.

Tripp went on to describe what happened that fateful day. "Sarah was unusually jolly for her. In the evening, when we returned, we all donned our chore clothes and went to work. Sarah put on her working clothes, too, and had them on when she disappeared." Tripp said. "If she had meant to run away, she would have dressed up."

Henry Tripp continued to recall the events of the evening. "I came into the kitchen about nine o'clock. Sarah was paring potatoes, which was the last thing she had to do. I sat down in the sitting room and my wife sat next to me. We were both, I believe, reading. My daughter had gone up the road aways on her wheel to call on Mrs. Daly."

Cycling had become a national craze among trendy and independently spirited women. Iva had recently purchased a new bicycle–often called a wheel–which she used to visit her neighbor. The elderly Mrs. Daly lived only a house away on Noodleton Road towards Mapleton station. Her unmarried daughter Alice lived with her and was just five years older than Iva Tripp.

Tripp continued with his story. "After a minute or so we heard the kitchen door open and then close. My wife, after about ten minutes, looked at the clock and seeing that it was about nine o'clock went to the door and called Sarah. She got no answer. She called again several times but received no reply."

Mr. Tripp confirmed that this was the last time he or his wife could account for their adopted daughter. "We never saw Sarah alive again," he said.

The reporter inquired why Sarah might have left so abruptly.

"Sarah was often in the habit of going out on the road and racing with my daughter, Sarah running and the other on her wheel," Tripp answered, referring to his daughter Iva who had ridden her bicycle down to the Dalys. "It is my belief that she went out to meet her and was carried off by somebody."

Though there had been speculation about foul play, this was the first indication that Mr. Tripp had given that he no longer believed Sarah had left the property of her own accord.

"My wife went across to the home of our son, who lives just over the way, but they had not seen Sarah."

Tripp then described the exhaustive search made that night. Both he and his son had knocked on doors and searched up and down the creek. "If I had known how it was going to turn out I would have aroused the entire neighborhood, but I did not like to wake up all the people who had gone to bed. We looked all night ourselves, and the next morning my son located Sarah, but she was dead."

The reporter asked him to elaborate on what he believed happened.

"It is my theory that the girl was carried off by somebody, for what purpose I don't know and perhaps murdered. It is as much of a mystery to me and my family as it is to anybody else."

The absence of blood on the engine and tracks still perplexed Cleveland. After consulting his books, the coroner learned that when a limb is severed by a train wheel and the arteries are crushed together, this might prevent excessive bleeding. However, this was only one possibility. Cleveland was committed to exploring them all and was not averse to seeking views more expert than his own.

Dr. Willis M. Pettit would have an opinion on the matter. He was the physician whom Cleveland called to examine Sarah's remains on the day her body had been discovered. Like Cleveland, Dr. Pettit was a native of Niagara County and a fellow Lockport Union School graduate. He also earned a degree from the New York College of Homeopathic Medicine.

Dr. Pettit had a particular interest in applying his medical knowledge to solve cases. It was the dawn of the golden era of forensic science, and he had no doubt been influenced by some of its pioneers. Chemist James Marsh discovered a test for Arsenic in 1836, Physician Ludwig Teichmann developed a method to confirm the presence of blood in 1853, and Police Officer Juan Vucetich designed a system for identifying fingerprints in 1892. But Dr. Pettit had studied blood under a microscope in a criminal investigation almost two decades before Edmond Locard–the father of modern forensic science–built the first crime lab.

Like Sherlock Holmes and Dr. Watson, Cleveland and Dr. Pettit worked together on more than a few inquests since Cleveland took the role of Niagara County Coroner in 1892. One case of note that surely stuck in both their memories, the papers had dubbed the 'Johnson Creek Episode'. It began when an old sack was uncovered while moving a barn in Hartland. A story began to circulate that the sack contained the remains of a small child hidden away to guard a secret. When Coroner Cleveland heard the mysterious tale, he headed out to investigate along with Pettit and another doctor. The team was taken to the spot where the bag was buried. Upon examining the contents, the coroner discovered it was filled with heads and bodies of frogs from the nearby Johnson Creek. The story of foul play was later believed to be nothing more than a joke.

Most of their investigations were less lighthearted. The Mumford case seemed to be turning darker each day. When Pettit heard of the lack of blood at the scene, he believed it to be an indication that Sarah was dead before the train hit her.

15
Amelia

Amelia's father came home from church, ate the meal she had prepared for him, and went straight to the barn. He managed to do it without either looking at or speaking to Amelia. It had been that way since Ricca had told him about Amelia's condition.

Ricca had gone to visit her friend, Freda Graff, after church. Mrs. Graff immigrated as a widow with a 10-year-old daughter in 1892 to marry a widower with a boy of his own. She only spoke German, so Ricca had helped her to adjust. The two became good friends.

Amelia received two pleasant surprises from her mother when she returned from the Graffs. First, was the news that Freda Graff's eldest daughter, Mary Shaffer, planned to visit Amelia. Mary Shaffer and Amelia were the same age and the two had become friendly.

The second surprise was the Sunday edition of the *Buffalo Times*, purchased and read by Mary's new husband George.

"Mrs. Graff has no use for a newspaper," Ricca said. "She meant to use it to wrap fish, but I convinced her to let me take the better part of it for you to read to your father."

Amelia held the newspaper like it contained instructions for a buried treasure. Her eyes quickly gravitated to a headline—written in all capital letters—that read "Sarah Mumford

Kidnapped and Murdered." The line directly below contained the disclaimer "So Henry Tripp, Her Foster Father Believes."

Amelia did not want to wait for her father to read the rest. She wanted to run to her room and spread the paper over her bed and read every word, especially the story about Sarah. But then she considered how nice it would be to share the story with him.

As a young girl, Amelia often read the paper to her father. Ricca said it was to get her to practice her reading. Amelia did not need to be tricked into reading. She devoured every book or print she could get her hands on. But she most enjoyed reading aloud as her father sat back in his chair, pipe in hand. He would sometimes stop her mid-sentence to make a short comment or two. It was about as talkative as her father ever got. Amelia suspected the arrangement was her mother's way of bringing her husband the news, without pointing to the fact he could not read it himself.

Amelia looked down at the paper she clutched in her hands and saw her protruding belly. She doubted her father would let her read to him now.

16
Sarah's Story
June 22, 1899

Nineteenth-century coroners wielded a great deal of power. Suspicious deaths had to pass through them first, and the wheels of justice did not turn until the coroner found a crime. This made the politically charged office ripe for corruption.

In the Gilded Age, corruption permeated American politics. Led by party bosses, elections were bought through a system of patronage and promised positions. Those awarded jobs were often eager to return favors. The federal government had enacted a merit system for civil servant positions as part of late nineteenth-century political reform. But in local politics, the spoils system still reigned. Local party affiliation had more to do with favoritism than ideology. Beyond prized political appointments, favors exchanged along party lines were standard for the day.

Though Cleveland was a Democrat through and through, he had earned respect across party lines for the enthusiastic execution of his duties. Before he became a coroner, he served as the Chief Engineer of the Lockport Fire Department for two years. The chief engineer, though appointed by the mayor, was nominated by delegates at the firemen's convention. Like everything Cleveland did, he carried out his position with absolute commitment. This became apparent during a large fire that threatened several Lockport mills in 1892.

"Chief Engineer Cleveland was in the midst of the fray throughout the fight against the fire. His courage and coolness were admirable. He will carry away several scars and bruises as souvenirs of gallant conduct this morning," reported the *Lockport Daily Sun.*

At the 1893 firemen's convention, Chief Cleveland announced that he was not a candidate for reelection. Still, half of the eighteen delegates cast their vote for Cleveland. That he still received the support he did after declining the nomination showed the high esteem in which he was held. But Cleveland already had his hands full as the new Niagara County Coroner.

The inquest reconvened at two o'clock on Thursday afternoon. Once again, the eight jurors gathered in a room at Prudden Brother's Undertaking. By order of Coroner Cleveland, the proceedings took place behind closed doors. Even members of the press were shut out. This fueled speculation. Reporters conjectured that the coroner knew the case would be turned over for prosecution and did not want to 'tip his hand.' But it might have also been Cleveland's way of allowing reluctant witnesses to speak freely without fear of repercussions. Closed proceedings meant Cleveland also denied admission to the Tripp family.

Cleveland had subpoenaed numerous witnesses to testify before the jury. He intended to examine each one separately. He informed the press that it would take a considerable amount of time. It was unknown if he braced the jury for what they were about to hear.

Mrs. George Miller, a neighbor of the Tripps, testified that she had last seen Sarah Mumford on the 25th of that April. She relayed to the jury the circumstances of that encounter:

Sarah came over to the house that day searching for some ducks that she thought had wandered over to the Miller's property. She said they belonged to Lauren Tripp and had gotten loose. Sarah was trying to retrieve them before they noticed she was gone.

Mrs. Miller described the girl as dressed in rags and wearing shoes that were worn and torn. Sarah had appeared nervous and implied that she was not supposed to be there talking. She did, however, fill Mrs. Miller in on her unhappy circumstances. According to Mrs. Miller, Sarah told her that the Tripps treated her awfully. Not only had they prohibited her from talking to the neighbors, but they also refused to let her write to her sisters in Rochester. Sarah confided in Mrs. Miller that she planned to leave the Tripps as soon as she came of age. She believed she would be entitled to $200 and some furniture to start a new life.

Mrs. Miller's husband George also testified. He claimed that for the past eleven months, Sarah had not been allowed to talk to any neighbors. The Tripps stopped sending her to school and kept her hidden from sight. Mr. Miller told the panel that he had been concerned about the child, so he notified the truant officer. He testified that a truant officer named Cramer had tried to get Sarah to school, but the Tripps claimed they taught her at home, so the matter was dropped.

Initially, Sarah attended Pendleton School number four on Mapleton Road. The young girl walked to the one-room schoolhouse located less than a half mile from the Tripp farmhouse. Her attendance at the school was sporadic. But on the day the photographer came to take the class picture in 1896, Sarah came to school to join the other students in the photo.

In the fall of 1897, the *Lockport Daily Journal* reported that Matilda Tripp was quite sick. Henry Tripp claimed that Sarah stopped attending school to help more at home because of Mrs. Tripp's illness. But the Tripps did not just keep Sarah from school; she also stopped attending church.

The testimony of the Millers would be disturbing, but nothing compared with what the jurors would learn next.

Elmer Cooler, a former farmhand, took the makeshift stand. He confirmed that Sarah was often not permitted to go to school or call on neighbors. But he also testified that he had seen Sarah mistreated by Mr. and Mrs. Tripp. He swore that he saw Sarah tied up and whipped with a large rope. Jurors shifted uncomfortably in their seats as he described how the poor girl cried for mercy. Cooler had also seen Mrs. Tripp drag Sarah across the yard. Sarah fought back. But every time she kicked; the older women would hit her across the face. At least once, he stated, Sarah was locked in the corn crib as punishment for not completing her chores.

Several other laborers who had worked on the Tripp farm supported this testimony.

Other neighbors came forward to share their stories of Sarah's mistreatment. According to the testimony, Sarah had endured repeated abuse. Some witnesses described her being left to hang by her wrists in the backyard shed.

The LeValleys, who were former neighbors of the Tripps, also came forward to testify against them. Mrs. Lorenzo LeValley reported that Sarah was often whipped harder than a child should be. She testified that all the Tripps, except for Lauren Tripp's wife Carrie, treated Sarah badly. Mrs. LeValley then told the jury that as of late, even Carrie Tripp had been prohibited from speaking to the girl.

Carrie Tripp had joined the family in February of 1896 when Lauren left for Michigan to wed the sister-in-law of his eldest sister Addie. Afterward, Lauren brought his new bride home with him. According to Mrs. LeValley, Carrie had treated Sarah kindly. Thirteen years separated their ages, but Sarah and Carrie had some things in common. Both came from towns called Palmyra, though in different states, and both Carrie and Sarah had left behind sisters. Most significantly, both were outsiders in the Tripp home.

Mr. LeValley followed his wife's testimony. He reiterated the inhumane treatment of Sarah at the hands of the Tripps. But his evident disdain for Henry Tripp went beyond the treatment of his adopted daughter. He indicated a pattern of violence in the Tripp family. He told the jurors of a time that Henry Tripp and his son Lauren had assaulted an 86-year-old man named Daniel Deffienbacher. According to Mr. LeValley, the old farmer almost died from the assault.

LeValley was not the only witness to attest that Henry Tripp was a quarrelsome neighbor. Jurors heard testimony that Henry Tripp had once been accused of poisoning chickens that he believed had poached some of his feed. But LeValley had his own reasons for disliking the Tripp family that might have colored his testimony.

A great many witnesses were willing to testify in the proceedings, but not all had terrible things to say about the family. Two of Tripp's hired men took the stand on their employers' behalf. They refuted the accusations that Sarah had been mistreated or improperly punished.

When the inquest adjourned, it was clear that another session had to be scheduled for the following Thursday. This new evidence, as horrid as it was, did not implicate anyone directly in Sarah's death. In fact, the dreadful details of Sarah's life might have supported suicide. But one thing became clear. The Tripps were not telling the whole truth. But just what was it they were hiding? If coroner Cleveland wanted to build a case, he needed to find the connection between the neighbor's testimony and what happened on the night of June 8th.

The pressure on Coroner Cleveland mounted. Most of the criticism stemmed from the fact that he insisted the proceeding be closed, which the press challenged his right to do. But stories coming out of North Tonawanda urged a deeper examination. Reports from that city alleged that "the girl was murdered by a person who had motives for the crime and her body was placed across the rail to throw authorities off the scent of the true state of affairs," the *Buffalo Review* wrote.

Reporters hit Cleveland with a barrage of questions as soon as he left the undertakers. Cleveland indicated he would make efforts to notify any family Sarah might still have in Rochester of her death. He refused to release any testimony for publication. But when asked, he admitted that the case was turning in a grave direction. Cleveland still had many things to sort out. One of those things, he told the newsmen, would require the testimony of someone who lived a good distance away.

Three evenings later, another prosperous farmer went to bed as usual in his Pendleton home. The next morning his son discovered the 54-year-old hanging from a ladder in his barn with a rope around his neck. Since Coroner Cleveland was otherwise occupied, a physician from Martinsville in North Tonawanda was called to take his place. Dr. Helwig discovered a bullet hole in the farmer's head and a revolver on the barn floor. The peculiar circumstances warranted a closer look. Dr. Helwig empaneled a jury.

The farmer's wife stated that he had been acting queerly the few days preceding his death. It took two weeks for the jury to render a verdict of suicide. They concluded that the well-respected farmer came to his death by hanging and a bullet shot in his head by his own hand.

It was uncharacteristic of Cleveland to allow someone else to investigate a death in his jurisdiction. But the Sarah Mumford investigation consumed his time. Coroner Cleveland had many more people he wanted to question.

17
Amelia

Amelia heard the wagon before she heard her mother.

"George Shafer's here with Mary," Ricca called. Amelia was already at the door.

The two girls embraced.

"George coming in?" Ricca asked.

"Nein," Mary said. "He's got errands in town today,"

"I thought we could sit outside," Amelia said, "to get some fresh air."

Ricca started to protest.

"No one will see," Amelia said. 'We'll stay in the back." Amelia didn't wait for Ricca's response. She took her friend's arm and walked her toward the back door.

"Well, offer Mary a drink first," Ricca said.

"Danka," Mary said. "Maybe later."

Amelia led Mary to a bench her grandfather had made from two tree stumps. The bench was shaded by a willow tree she helped plant as a child by sticking a twig in the ground. It had grown so big her father had threatened to cut it down. The two girls sat next to each other on the bench. Their long skirts mingled at their feet.

"How was the wedding?" Amelia asked. "I'm sorry I couldn't be there."

"Nice, Ma and I made my dress." Mary and George had been married quickly. Amelia knew better than to ask why.

"I bet it was pretty," Amelia said. "How's Herman?" Mary's stepbrother was only two years older than the girls.

"Herman left for Chicago," Mary said. "He sent a letter saying he is thinking about joining the Navy."

"The Navy?"

"He wrote that with the war in the Philippines, he'll be sent to the other side of the world. You know Herman, he always wanted to see the world."

Amelia nodded. It seemed to her that just this past Christmas, all anyone had talked about was America's victory in the war with Spain. Then, most people she heard were in favor of supporting Cuba's struggle for independence. But defeating the Spanish meant the U.S. gained new territory far from home. Now the people of the Philippine Republic were fighting U.S. forces for the right to be independent. Americans were divided. If Amelia were allowed an opinion, she would say let the people be free. But Herman would probably say it was more complicated than that.

"Have you heard about the Tripp girl?" Mary asked. Amelia was thankful she changed the subject. She spent the morning thinking of a way to steer the conversation to Sarah Mumford without sounding like a gossiper. Mary made it easy.

"People are saying she might have been murdered," Mary whispered the word murdered.

"Murdered," Amelia thought for a moment. "Well, I didn't think she committed suicide."

"George has been buying the *Times* every day so we can follow it." Mary leaned closer. "There are all kinds of theories."

"Like what?" Amelia had been thinking more about what did not happen than what did.

"Mr. Tripp says she was kidnapped,"

"I read that part," Amelia said. She had not given much consideration to Mr. Tripp's theory. It disturbed her to think a murderer was at large in Pendleton.

"Well, one theory is that she broke away from her kidnapper and ran. Then she tripped on the track and was killed by the fall." Mary said. "George thinks that's ridiculous."

"I think I agree," Amelia said.

Mary placed her hand over her heart. "George thinks a tramp must have criminally assaulted her and left her dead body on the track to cover it up."

"Why would he think that?" Amelia asked.

"Because they say it must have been someone who knew the trains well," Mary said. "The way they left the body where the trainmen wouldn't see it."

"Anyone who lives near the tracks knows the trains." Amelia shuddered. *What if someone was attacking young girls in delicate conditions?*

"That's what I thought," Mary said. "I've heard other things that the paper won't print. George said it's because they can't prove them true."

This time Amelia leaned in to listen.

"People who would know say that the Tripp family only adopted her to be their servant and they wouldn't have to pay her," Mary said. "And they treated her cruelly."

It made Amelia sad that Sarah was not treated like family, but it did not surprise her.

"I heard from a friend who knew a girl that lives in Mapleton that she saw, with her own two eyes, Sarah hanging by her thumbs in a room off the back kitchen," Mary said.

"That's horrible. Why would they do that?"

"Who knows? Mrs. Tripp would whip her for doing the littlest thing wrong," Mary said. "Everybody in their neighborhood knew it. They just told their children to walk on the other side of the road."

"Maybe Mrs. Tripp meant to punish her and accidentally killed her," Amelia said.

"I don't think so," Mary said. "Mrs. Tripp is frail and sickly, not to mention old, and Sarah was a big girl."

"Is that so," Amelia thought for a moment. "Then she would have to have done it from behind." Amelia became amused by the idea of figuring it out. "I have a theory."

Mary scooted a little closer.

"What if Sarah was in the kitchen paring potatoes just like Mr. Tripp said in the paper." Amelia began. "But she wasn't doing it well enough to suit the old woman. So, Mrs. Tripp started to give her a tongue-lashing. And maybe Sarah even snapped back, which would have enraged Mrs. Tripp." Amelia paused to think. "Maybe she reached for something nearby, like a frying pan, and whacked her in the back of her head?" She paused again, this time for the effect. "Sarah slumped to the floor. When Mr. Tripp realized what his wife had done, he dragged Sarah out back. And that's when he devised a plan to cover it up."

Mary Shafer looked at her friend curiously. "Aren't you afraid?"

"Of Mrs. Tripp?"

Before Mary could answer, Amelia realized she meant the baby. "It doesn't do any good to worry about it," she said. Amelia believed this, but it didn't keep her from worrying just the same.

"Have you heard from him?"

"Not yet," Amelia said. She had not heard from the baby's father since she told him of her condition. That was months ago.

"If I were you, I would be terrified," Mary said. "I don't think I could do it alone."

Amelia knew her friend might be thinking about her own circumstances as much as hers.

"It will turn out fine," Amelia said. Mary's face looked like she did not believe her. Amelia shifted in her seat hoping to change the subject. "You're right, I don't really think Mrs. Tripp did it. What do you think?"

Mary smiled. "George never asks," she said. "I think she snuck out to meet her lover."

Amelia thought about it for a few seconds.

"I'm afraid I can't agree with that theory," Amelia said.

Mary chuckled. "What do you know?"

"I know she was dressed in her chore clothes, Mr. Tripp said so," Amelia said. "Would you have gone to see George in your chore clothes?"

Mary laughed harder. "I can't imagine ever doing that before we were married, but he sees me all the time in my chore clothes now." The two girls laughed together.

Suddenly Amelia realized they were laughing. She had been using Sarah as a distraction like it was a game. It was wrong to find amusement in Sarah's tragedy. Amelia had not known the girl in life, but she felt like she knew her now. They had shared the same plight. But Sarah was dead, and whatever injustice she had been dealt, Amelia felt as if it had happened to her.

"I wish I could solve the case for real," Amelia said. "For Sarah."

18
Sarah's Story
June 29, 1899

Farmers searched the sky for a sign of relief from the drought. The press looked to Cleveland for something new about the Mumford case to print. The inquest reconvened on Monday, and all the newspapers could gather was that as many as fifteen witnesses had been sworn in and what they had to say was sensational. Cleveland would not reveal a word of it.

"You may say this:" he told reporters, "the case appears to be a grave one, and clouds seem to be gathering."

On Thursday, the eight jurors continued to hear testimony from a parade of witnesses. Cleveland attempted to piece together a timeline of the night of June 8th, when Sarah had reportedly gone missing. They had established that Sarah had been struck by the train at midnight. According to Mr. and Mrs. Tripp, she was last seen at 9:00 p.m. What accounted for the three hours in between was what the jurors hoped to learn.

Horace Chadsey, the Presbyterian minister who lived on a farm near the Tripp's property, testified as to what he saw that night. He told the jurors that on the night in question, at about 10:00 p.m., Lauren Tripp came to his house to ask if he had seen the girl. According to Chadsey, Lauren had been driving a horse-drawn wagon.

Several other witnesses testified to having seen Lauren Tripp driving about in the family's canopy-topped wagon that evening. At least one witness reported seeing his sister Iva with him.

Chadsey continued his testimony. According to the minister, at around 11:30 p.m. he had seen the same wagon heading back towards Shawnee crossing. He was positive it was the Tripp wagon he had seen.

Willis Olds provided some of the most damaging testimony. The 27-year-old lived with his young wife and his parents in the town of Cambria. The Olds' homestead was located between the Tripp farm and where Sarah's body had been found. He testified that he not only saw the Tripp rig on the night of June 8th but that the curtains on the canopied wagon were drawn. Willis also stated that he saw the Tripps the next morning in their light buggy. He thought it odd "that they should change wagons in the middle of the search for the missing girl." But what was most disturbing came next. He swore that he heard Mr. Tripp explain that the canopy wagon was stained in blood from transporting a calf carcass to the butcher in Tonawanda.

Other witnesses stated that Lauren had told them he was looking for Sarah, who had been missing since 9:00. One reported that Lauren Tripp claimed that evening that he thought he heard hollering coming from the woods near the track.

Charles Wollaber also testified to the events of June 8th. The 43-year-old explained to the jury that he lived on Comstock farm, less than a quarter mile from Shawnee crossing. He told them that he saw a canopy wagon near the crossing late in the evening the night of Sarah's disappearance. Not only did Wollaber's testimony corroborate previous testimony, but it possibly placed one of the Tripps near–what they believed to be–the scene of the crime.

The witness testimony added new links to the chain of evidence. Cleveland might have recalled an interview with a railroad worker about the location of Sarah Mumford's body. The trainman remarked that the body was in a spot that was blocked from the engineer's view by a pole. If it had been either a bit closer or farther from the road, it would have been spotted.

"If anyone had desired to put that body where they wanted it run over, they could not have chosen a better spot," the railroad man said. "It looks to me that the body was placed on the track with great care and after some little study of the situation."

Cleveland might have wondered if the positioning of the body indicated something else. People speculated that whoever placed Sarah on the track wished to conceal her identity. But the standard train rail stood more than six inches high. The additional distance between the wheel and the axel provided a clearance between the belly of a train and the track bed. If the culprit wanted to conceal Sarah's identity, they would have laid her head across the rail. This was not the case. The train wheels crushed Sarah's pelvis.

The inquest adjourned until the following Monday. Cleveland needed to secure more witnesses. He returned to his home on Waterman Street to prepare for a morning train ride to Rochester.

19
Amelia

Thursday was laundry day. It used to be Monday, but Amelia's father took work away from home on Mondays. Her mother needed him to help her lift the heavy pots since Amelia could no longer help. Ricca had to alter her entire chore schedule. So now, they did the wash on Thursday.

When Amelia was a small child, she never minded laundry day. She liked the attention and fuss required because it was something the women in her family all did together. She dreamed of the day she would be tall enough to stand elbow to elbow at the tubs with her mother and sisters.

But it had not turned out that way. Now she dreaded laundry day and it only worsened with her condition. Amelia sat over a pot of steaming water, stirring her father's trousers, her shoulders stiffening with each turn. Strands of her light brown hair stuck to the side of her face. Ricca stepped in from outside carrying an armful of damp clothes. She set them down and peered at her daughter.

"They need turned over, not stirred," her mother said. "Here, let me do it." Ricca took the pole from Amelia and brushed her away from the vat. "Why don't you read to me for a while? It makes the work go faster."

Amelia, grateful for her mother's burst of kindness, hurried to find the newspaper that she received over a week ago. She had read it at least once each day since.

"What should I read," she asked anxiously.

"You choose," her mother answered.

"I could read about the Tripp girl," Amelia offered. Ricca could read, and Amelia knew she had seen the paper. But Amelia had been afraid to talk with her about the story since her mother discouraged gossip.

"It's long, where should I start?" she asked.

"At the beginning," Ricca said. "We have a week's worth of wash to get done."

Amelia spread the paper out and began to read.

"The Mapleton Mystery grows in depth and interest. Henry Tripp, the father of Sarah Mumford, the dead girl, has given the *Times* a statement, in which he expresses it is his belief that the girl was kidnapped and probably murdered on the evening of June 8th."

Amelia paused. "It says here that she is sometimes called Mary Ross," Amelia said. "Why do you think she had two names?"

"Sometimes the paper gets it wrong," Ricca said.

Amelia continued to read. "The peculiar features connected with the case have aroused curiosity-not to say suspicion-of the simple country folk, and authorities of Niagara County are doing their utmost to sift the matter to the bottom."

"Hmph," said Ricca. "Seems simple country folk know more about it than the authorities."

Amelia nodded in agreement. She read about the testimony of the engineer and the other trainmen.

"Read the part about what Mr. Tripp had to say," Ricca said.

Amelia slid her finger down the column and stopped at Henry Tripp's account of the evening Sarah went missing.

"I came into the kitchen about nine o'clock. Sarah was paring potatoes, which was the last thing she had to do."

"Paring potatoes? Ricca shook her head. "Must be nice to have so much that you can throw away perfectly good potato peels."

Amelia laughed a little at her mother and kept on reading.

"The suicide theory had been advanced." Amelia read. "Mr. Tripp, when asked about this, said the girl had never threatened to kill herself. She had not said anything about running away from home. All the members of the Tripp family said that the girl was treated just like one of them, and never had any cause for complaint." Amelia set the paper to the side.

"He's not telling the truth," Amelia said. "Mary Shafer and Aunt Katherine said they treated her horribly."

Ricca started to lift the heavy wet pants out of the pot one at a time. Amelia got up to hold the empty tub she was transferring them to.

"I bet that is why they decided to keep her hidden.," Amelia said, "to keep her from telling others how she was treated."

"Could be," Ricca said.

"But all those neighbors knew, and they didn't do anything to help her." Amelia felt sad and angry for Sarah.

"Wasn't much they could do. Most people mind their own business."

"Well, they don't seem to be minding their own business now," Amelia said.

Ricca appeared to be too focused on the rest of the laundry to pay attention anymore to the conversation.

"I wonder, "Amelia said. "What else is Mr. Tripp lying about? Maybe he knows more about Sarah's death than he lets on."

"Enough," her mother said, shaking her finger. "This is not your concern. A girl is dead, and you obsess about death more than is healthy."

Amelia had never considered that she was obsessed with death. True, ever since she had read a short story about the great detective Sherlock Holmes, she was intrigued by a good murder mystery. But her mother was wrong. She was not interested in death. She abhorred it. The way it crept into your life uninvited and insensibly robbed families of their loved ones. No, what interested Amelia was the notion that there were clues within death that might make some sense of it all. That is what she could not turn away from. What she was obsessed with was finding answers.

20
Sarah's Story
July 3, 1899

July began hot and dry. Farmers worried if they did not receive rain soon, the crops would suffer. But the inquest into the mysterious death of Sarah Mumford had dragged on longer than the drought.

Cleveland must have started to believe his methods were working. Piece by piece, the evidence was leading him to a solution. But the answer to the mystery of Sarah Mumford's death was far from complete.

The *Buffalo Times* pointed out that no motive for the crime had been suggested. "Whether one can be brought to the surface or not, is a question the future alone can determine." The *Times* reported quite prophetically.

The coroner's jury reconvened on Monday afternoon and again the proceedings were closed. Newspapers clamored to discover the identities of the witnesses. Over the preceding weekend, Mrs. Thompson, the wife of the Mapleton's station master, visited North Tonawanda. There she told others that she had been subpoenaed to testify at the inquest. She implied her evidence before the jury would cause a sensation. But she did not want to reveal any details of her testimony.

As the *Niagara Sun* reported, "Coroner Cleveland desires the strictest secrecy until he has concluded the examination and investigated the numerous rumors regarding the girl's treatment before her death and whether or not she was dead before being struck by the train."

The pieces were finally starting to drop in place. But before he could unravel the circumstances of her death, Cleveland needed to resolve another mystery. Who was Sarah Mumford and what exactly was her relationship with the Tripp family?

21
Amelia

It was the last July fourth of the century. Amelia watched her father hang the worn but cherished flag that belonged to Uncle Fritz. Her father continued the tradition in his brother's absence. Their humble homestead had celebrated thirty-one Independence Days with Old Glory waving on the front porch.

Amelia remembered the celebrations from her childhood. Her family of aunts, uncles, cousins, and a few friends would gather to share a picnic supper with a rousing bonfire to end the evening. The children chased fireflies, the men toasted, and Uncle Fritz would make a speech. He had a habit of droning on about the past, whenever he drank too much. He told the same story of how he came here by himself from the old country as a young man and joined the Union Army. He offered no details of the war other than that he injured his ankle. And that when he returned home to Pendleton, the rest of the family had arrived from Germany to greet him.

Uncle Fritz became a citizen because of his service. It also cleared a path for his father and brother to do the same. Not more than a few years after they arrived, Amelia's Grandpa Charles purchased his first piece of land and built the house her family lived in now.

"How about that," she could hear Uncle Fritz slur, "a man born into serfdom, a slave to the land, becoming a landowner in a free country."

Most of her big family had died or moved away. That fourth of July it would be just the three of them. Her mother offered to make a strawberry cake to make it seem more like a picnic. Amelia did not feel much like celebrating. Today, she felt especially cooped up and confined.

A homemade firecracker popped in the distance. People all over the town of Pendleton would be gathering to commemorate Independence Day. Amelia thought about Sarah Mumford. She wondered if she ever had a chance to celebrate anything before her life was lost.

22
Sarah's Story
July 6, 1899

On Thursday morning, Coroner Cleveland stepped outside onto a dampened street. It had rained steadily throughout the night, but not nearly enough to please the farmers. Cleveland had subpoenaed a man from the Rochester Poor Department. The civil servant traveled seventy miles from Rochester to help the jurors resolve the mystery behind Sarah Mumford's early life and her relation to the Tripp family. The coroner hoped his testimony would satisfy the drought of information about the girl's identity. The press had referred to her as Sarah A. Mumford, Sarah Tripp, Mary Ross, Mary Mumford, and Mary Tripp. None of these names were correct.

Once again, the jurors convened in the Prudden Brothers' establishment. John Calder took the stand. Mr. Calder explained his role as bookkeeper of the poor department for the City of Rochester. He had received the appointment to that position in 1891 and reported to Richard Gardiner, Overseer of the Poor. By order of Gardiner, Calder, not Henry Tripp, took Sarah from the orphanage on April 22, 1895.

Calder did not work for the Rochester Orphan Asylum, so how much he knew about Sarah's early days was unknown. However, the records showed that Sarah's birth date was September 2nd. The most recent and consistent documentation listed her birth year as 1883, though earlier records showed her younger. This meant that she was no more than fifteen when she died. The admission records also showed that Sarah had a family, and she had not been an orphan. The records listed Sarah's parents as John and Daisy Mumford.

Sarah's mother was born Cora M. Wilbur–the oldest of nine children–she often went by the nickname Daisy. She married John H. Mumford and had her first child when she was a teenager. They began their marriage in the small town of Palmyra, thirty miles east of Rochester. In 1880, they lived with their 1-year-old daughter Grace. John Mumford worked as a teamster–a job known for long hours and minimal pay. Both parents had families living nearby in Palmyra. In 1885, they baptized 6-year-old Grace and 4-year-old Kittie in the Zion Church. Sarah Lavinia Mumford's baptism occurred at the Easter vigil in 1887.

They eventually moved the family to the city of Rochester which meant John would be closer to work. The Mumford girls attended the Industrial School on Exchange Street. The school had been established to serve destitute children. The institution's original mission was "to gather into the school, vagrant and destitute children, who from the vice of their parents, are unable to attend the public schools, and who gather a precarious livelihood by begging and pilfering." By the 1890s they also served children of the working poor and those whose parents both worked. Children as young as kindergarten received an education that included trade skills like sewing and cooking for girls.

The urban neighborhoods where the Mumford family could afford to live were not always safe for children. On an afternoon in 1890, a sinister man approached Sarah and Kittie on their way home from school. He persuaded 9-year-old Kittie to follow him behind a lumber pile where he assaulted her. Several men heard her screams, interrupted the crime, and apprehended her assailant. Kittie became so distraught she refused to go home and hid at a neighbor's house. The poor girl believed she had done something wrong and would be punished.

Soon after the incident, Sarah's grandmother died leaving Sarah's mother Cora's younger siblings orphaned. Around this time John Mumford chose to desert his family. Single mothers had few options, government assistance was nonexistent. The work available to women required long hours with low pay. Desperate, Sarah's mother placed the children temporarily in the Rochester Orphan Asylum in March of 1891. She gave the orphanage $1 each for their care. But they did not remain there long.

By 1892, Sarah's mother moved in with a man and had all three of her daughters back in the home. She also took care of two of her younger siblings. But the situation did not remain stable. On June 21, 1893, Sarah's mother appeared before the Rochester Police Court on charges of drunkenness. Judge Ernst gave her parole for good behavior but ordered the girls placed back in the Rochester orphanage.

The three Mumford girls had an Aunt Sarah and a Grandmother Lavinia, on their father's side, living in Palmyra. But Aunt Sarah, a widow, struggled to feed her own five children and her elderly mother by taking in laundry. In March of 1894, a Palmyra farmer and his wife–Mr. and Mrs. George Cornwell–took Sarah and Kittie into their home. Cornwell then placed Sarah with his adult son and his wife. Neither girl adjusted to either home. After three months, the Cornwells returned both Sarah and Kittie to the orphanage.

Because Sarah had been placed in the Orphanage by order of a city judge, her care became the financial responsibility of the City of Rochester.

Before 1875, the business of child saving was purely private. But when New York passed a law removing children from poorhouses, the state acknowledged some responsibility for the impoverished children. Since a system of private orphanages already existed, there was no need to reinvent a new one. Poor departments simply paid a subsidy to the orphanages for each child they placed.

At the time, the fees paid to the asylum by the City of Rochester's poor department amounted to more than ten times Mr. Calder's monthly salary. The bookkeeper might have felt pressure to lighten the roles. However, the poor department faced the same challenges the orphanages faced in finding proper homes for children. Calder had other responsibilities and his meager $900 a year did not provide for roaming the state inspecting homes.

In 1894, Reverend William Jarvis Maybee and his assistant Mr. Lent approached Gardiner and the board of managers at the Rocester Orphan Asylum with a proposal. Maybee claimed to be the superintendent of the New York Children's Homes Society. For a fee of $50 a head, he promised to place children in homes across the state.

Something about the two men tripped a protective nerve for the ladies of the board. "The Board of Managers would put itself upon record as opposed, individually and collectively, to this method of procuring homes for the children temporarily placed in its care. The system as presented to the board by Mr. Lent," they wrote in their annual report, "seemed open to grave objections."

As overseer of the poor, Richard Gardiner saw something different. The city spent multiple times more than fifty dollars in boarding fees on average for each dependent child in their charge. Maybee's proposal seemed too good to be true. The year before Sarah was placed with the Tripp family, they turned five children over to Maybee despite the objections of the Orphanage's board.

Gardiner was not alone in his enthusiasm for Maybee's proposal. All over the state, Maybee earned the trust of poor departments and town officials alike. He and Lent went from town-to-town pitching to officials, speaking at churches, and collecting both donations and the names of families interested in taking an orphan.

It was unknown if Calder turned Sarah over to Maybee to be placed with the Tripp family or delivered her himself. Or how Henry Tripp connected with either of them. Perhaps he heard one of Lent or Maybee's spiels. The men had canvased churches in both Erie and Niagara Counties. Either way, most placement systems lacked time and resources to vet families and even fewer resources to check on children after they had been placed.

During the week that Calder took Sarah from the asylum, he took two other girls, ages eight and twelve, to be placed. The Asylum records do not indicate where either of them went. When he received scrutiny about Sarah's case, Calder assured the public that he did his best.

"I went to Pendleton and carefully examined into the character of Mr. and Mrs. Tripp and also asked the neighbors about them," Calder told a reporter. "The neighbors agreed with me that they were highly respected and that the girl would have a happy home with them." If he had conducted a careful examination, it would have been rare. Most people of the era assumed prosperity meant a good home.

Given the reports of Sarah's horrible abuse, the testimony of the agent left jurors wondering what life with the Tripps had really been like for Sarah. When Sarah first arrived at the Tripp household, she had not yet turned twelve. She joined a family of four adults. Both Lauren and Iva lived with their parents. Lauren was twenty-one and Iva twenty-nine. According to the accounts by neighbors, Sarah's role in the family seemed to be that of a servant. This might have been the expectation from the start. Sarah had mentioned to the Millers that she would receive $200 and furniture when she turned eighteen. Indentured contracts often had similar agreements. The Rochester Orphanage continued to broker indentured arrangements for their inmates until 1906. But this agreement appeared to have been made with the Overseer of the Poor. Sarah, only eleven at the time, would have had no say in the agreement. The contract would have bound her, nevertheless.

Calder did not know of the neighbors' concerns or any reports of abuse. He would not have had the means to check on Sarah. He claimed he had received a letter reporting her well-being.

"Some time ago, I received two letters from Sarah saying that she was perfectly happy and that she was enjoying every minute of her life with her adopted father and mother." But according to what Sarah told Mrs. Miller, the Tripps controlled whom she could write. Even Calder had to agree that the letter did not prove anything. "Of course, I do not know whether the girl wrote the letters voluntarily, but the writing, I am sure, was hers."

It turned out, the protective instincts of the Rochester Orphan Asylum's Board of Managers might have been on target. In 1897, the New York Board of Charities accused William Jarvis Maybee of 'baby farming', a term used for placing out children for profit. They had previously rejected his application as a certified charity, so he lacked the authorization to conduct his business. Maybee accounted to no one. Most of the money collected in fees and donations went directly into his own pocket. He used it to build a new colonial-style home in a prosperous Syracuse suburb and furnished it handsomely.

Most disturbingly, Maybee could not produce records of where the children were placed or indentured. During the hearing, a member of the board of charities had questioned Maybee about a certain case.

"Your record does not show where they came from in many instances."

"No," Maybee replied.

"Have you any present knowledge of that child? Do you know whether it is alive or dead?"

"Well, I don't know," Maybee answered. "I could not say."

The Board member shifted the question to another child.

"Now, were you paid for taking that child over there; paid for taking the child and putting it in a home? As you call it."

"I was to receive pay."

"How much was your charge for the child?

"They were to pay $100 for that child."

After the hearing, Board member Dr. Stoddard wrote in his report. "The result has been that many of the older boys and girls have run away from their uncongenial or unsympathetic surroundings to become tramps or fall into criminal habits. With younger children much hardship has been experienced, and much mental and moral injury has resulted from their being improperly placed and left without subsequent supervision."

The State Board of Charities censured Maybee for his poor record-keeping and his method of profiting from his work. "The merchandising of helpless childhood for the purpose of enriching the coffers of the debased should no longer be permitted."

Shortly after, a family in Camden accused Maybee of kidnapping. The married woman had given Maybee fifty dollars to place her three youngest children in what she thought would be a temporary home while she recovered from an illness. A month later, Maybee refused to tell her where her children were. Maybee was arrested. But his financial situation afforded him a good attorney. He skirted the charges. Astonishingly, Maybee still had his share of supporters.

In March of 1898, the New York Senate debated a bill to regulate the practice of placing out children with a misdemeanor charge for violators like Maybee. The bill had failed the previous year. Board of Charities member Hibbard argued vehemently for its approval. He referred directly to the work of Maybee.

"According to this man's confession, a child born in lawful wedlock was taken from his mother by this man the very day of its birth," Hibbard said. "Which he received by way of compensation. He knew well, as all know, who deal with such young children, that the chances were greatly against the child's survival, and yet for the money he was willing to undertake this nefarious work."

The bill failed again. In May of that same year, a weaker version that did not include criminal charges for violators finally passed.

But the child welfare system, or lack thereof, was not on trial. Cleveland's focus was Sarah. The more he and his jury learned of Sarah's tragic life, the more they must have desired justice for her death.

That night the clouds opened, and the heavens poured down the much-needed rain.

23
Amelia

Friday crept by slowly. Amelia removed the hot iron from the fire and set it on the board her father fashioned for the chore. She grabbed a shirtwaist from the pile and stretched it out flat. Her belly hit the board at the wrong spot, so she had to take a step back. It made the work more difficult.

Her mother sat quietly reattaching a button to a pair of pants. They had said no more than a few words between them since the fourth of July. It seemed to Amelia that she annoyed her mother every time she spoke. So, she tried to limit her talking to matters of necessity.

Amelia occupied her mind thinking about Sarah Mumford. She remembered what Aunt Katherine had said about her coming from an orphanage in Rochester. A question arose in her mind that quickly escaped through her mouth.

"Why do you think Mr. Tripp went all the way to Rochester to get an orphan when there's an orphanage right in Lockport?" She asked her mother. Her mother did not respond immediately.

"Can't say," she said. Ricca did not look up from her mending.

"Maybe it was because of his reputation," Amelia thought aloud, "Maybe, they knew how mean he was."

“Not sure how much orphanages care about that,” Ricca said.

“They should,” Amelia said. “If he was as mean as everyone says he was, I think he might have killed her.”

A scowl crossed Ricca’s face and she set down the pants. “Mr. Tripp’s a quarrelsome man,” she said. “That doesn’t make him a murderer.”

Amelia was surprised to hear her mother speak ill of anyone.

“You know Mr. Tripp?”

Ricca resumed her sewing as if she was considering whether to answer. “Your father and I lived right next to him after we married,” she said. “Mr. Tripp and his wife still lived out on his father’s property near Beach Ridge.”

“What was he like?” Amelia asked.

Ricca hesitated for a minute. “Quarrelsome, like they say.” she finally answered. “And Annie lived as a domestic with the family living next door,” she continued. “But by then Henry and Matilda had their own place in Mapleton.”

Amelia had never heard this about her sister.

“Annie did?” said Amelia, “I don’t remember that.”

“That’s because you weren’t born yet,” Ricca stopped abruptly. Amelia noticed her mother’s expression change. They did not speak often of Annie anymore.

Ricca turned her focus back on the mending. Amelia continued ironing. The two women worked side by side in silence, giving Amelia more time to turn things over in her mind. Her sister Rachael had worked as a domestic for another family, but not until she was seventeen. Annie would have been much younger. If it was before Amelia was born, she would have only been fourteen when she lived with another family.

Amelia tried to picture it. She hoped the family had treated Annie better than the Tripp family treated Sarah.

24
Sarah's Story
July 10, 1899

Monday marked the fourth week of the coroner's inquest. The press harried Cleveland for dragging things out. The investigation into the death of Sarah Mumford had already lasted longer than most. But the more details the coroner uncovered, the more questions he had.

The testimony thus far created an unfavorable view of the Tripp family. It was time to give them the chance to reshape that image.

Henry's oldest daughter, Mrs. Addie Dersham, testified on her family's behalf.

The 38-year-old woman took the stand. She began to relay what she had seen the night of Sarah's death. This must have come as a shock to the jury, given the fact that she had not been in Mapleton village on June 8th. Addie Tripp Dersham testified that she was at her home near Pendleton Center when she had what she called a "presentiment." She went on to explain that while in bed, but still wide awake, she had a vision. Addie described to the jurors in detail a closed carriage with four men in it. To add to her testimony, she went on to say that she heard a voice tell her that trouble was in store for her and her family.

Addie had the jury's attention. She looked at them with an expression of gravity, declaring that the mystery would be solved when they found the men.

When questioned further, she insisted on the validity of her visions. Addie explained that she had a similar warning the night before her aunt died years ago. Addie's "presentment" seemed to corroborate her father's theory that Sarah had been abducted.

Next, it was her sister's turn to take the stand. Iva Tripp was not described as pretty, but she presented well. Her neatly arranged dark hair complemented her pale skin, and her eyes showed her intelligence. She spoke with confidence.

Iva entered the county teachers' institute in 1883. After completing her studies, she was assigned to the Mapleton school just down the road from her parents' home. But she did not remain there. She moved to and from several different schools across the county and landed in Cambria for the 1897 school year. But for the year just past, Iva took a hiatus from school teaching.

Earlier testimony had revealed that Iva treated Sarah cruelly and went out of her way to make the young girl's life uncomfortable. Iva Tripp's testimony did not add much information about what happened on June 8th. It also did little to dispel the testimony that she had been unkind to Sarah. But Iva revealed that the family had recently received word that Sarah's mother had been committed to an insane asylum in Rochester. She speculated that perhaps Sarah went temporarily insane when she wandered off that fateful evening.

It was true that Sarah's mother resided at the Rochester State Hospital for the Insane. The cause was unknown. In 1899, women were committed for reasons that spanned well beyond insanity. Admission records from at the time listed diagnoses such as religious excitement, abusive language, depressed menses, overexertion, and depression after the loss of a loved one. Anything that varied from her husband's expectation of proper wifely behavior might land a married woman in an asylum. The 1900 census listed Cora as married.

Sarah's discharge record at the Rochester Orphan Asylum indicated her father had died. It did not mention that her mother still lived in Rochester. It is doubtful it mattered. Parents had little rights to their children once they entered the orphanage. Even when voluntarily placed, the Rochester Orphan Asylum required parents to sign an agreement not to interfere with the children's care. Children reunited with their parents at the discretion of the charity. Most considered an indentured arrangement in a good home preferable to their own family and pauperism. Children taken by the court stood a smaller chance of reunification.

Even if Sarah's mother had tried to retrieve Sarah, it was unlikely she could have found her. The orphanage records do not mention the Tripp family.

It is possible the word that Iva spoke of came in a letter from one of Sarah's sisters via John Calder. Both 18-year-old Kittie and 20-year-old Grace lived in the Rochester area. They likely tried to find their younger sister. It is possible Grace and Kittie convinced the Poor Department agent to send their letters to the Tripps on their behalf. All of this would have taken diligence. But Grace and Kittie had found each other. There is evidence that they not only stayed connected but that they stayed in contact with their mother and her family for the remainder of their lives.

In 1900, Kittie and Grace lived together in a tenement building on Monroe Avenue. On Thanksgiving, a quarrel with neighbors over a shared water pipe escalated. A neighbor threatened Kittie with a knife, and she called the police. Angry that Kittie had him arrested, another neighbor woman tried to strangle Kittie. Her injuries sent her to the hospital. Her recovery took almost two months. Each time she showed improvement, she had a spell of Hysteria. Her condition—which today might be recognized as trauma-related—perplexed doctors and attorneys alike. She did not recover in time to testify against her assailants, so they went free. Grace and her new husband moved from the building so that Kittie would have a safe place to be discharged.

Sarah not only had family, but she also had roots and people who cared. Had Sarah been allowed to reconnect with her sisters, her life would not have been easy, but she would not have been alone.

Iva's testimony revealed that someone had tried to contact Sarah, and the Tripps interfered. Maybe they did not believe it was in their interest to allow Sarah to communicate with her family.

The hour grew late. Cleveland still had more witnesses to present, and a month had already passed since Sarah's death. He adjourned for the night with the plan to continue the following morning. The jurors and witnesses gathered before ten a.m. to continue the examination. But that session, too, had to be adjourned because Cleveland was called to Olcott. Though the Mumford inquest had consumed much of his time, there were other deaths in the county to tend to.

25
Amelia

Aunt Kathrine came by again on Wednesday bearing two gifts. One was a Tonawanda newspaper which she laid on the table. The other was a small bottle she placed in Amelia's palm.

"For when the baby comes," she whispered in her ear. The bottle contained a peach pit.

Amelia was glad to see her aunt so soon after her last visit. There was a time when they did not see her much at all. But she started coming around again after Uncle Fritz went to the old vet's home.

Amelia held up the tiny bottle and examined the carefully clean and dried pit. She did not know exactly what it meant but assumed it was some sort of charm. Aunt Katherine dabbled in such things. Some people thought she was a witch, or as they say in German, a Hexe. Amelia's mother insisted she was just superstitious.

"Katherine is a good Christian woman," Ricca claimed whenever the subject came up.

Once Aunt Katherine admitted to Amelia that she liked others to think she was a Hexe. "Sometimes, it is not so bad for people to fear you," she said. "A woman alone does what she has to."

Amelia's mother poured two cups of reheated coffee and sat at the Kitchen table.

"You do not share stories, Ja, I know." Aunt Katherine started. "But what they say happened to that girl, Ach."

Amelia listened, hoping her mother would take the bait.

"People say it has something to do with her being in a delicate way." Aunt Katherine said. She casually glanced toward Amelia's large belly. Then Katherine leaned toward Ricca. "The baby comes soon, ja?

"Soon," Ricca acknowledged.

"Still no father?" Aunt Katherine said. "The baby needs a name."

"Knople is a name," Ricca said.

"Ach, you should let the Knople name be disgraced by this scandal?"

"Well, it wouldn't be the first time someone in our family was involved in a scandal," Ricca said.

Aunt Kathrine bristled. "Na ja," she nodded. She paused and turned toward Amelia. "If the father of your baby does not do right, you tell your Tanta his name. He should be made sorry for this, Ja." This was the sort of thing Aunt Katherine liked to say and why her neighbors thought she was a Hexe. Amelia understood it was her aunt's strange way of showing support.

26
Sarah's Story
July 13, 1899

The inquest continued Thursday afternoon with the eight jurors once again gathering at Prudden Brothers Undertaking establishment. Cleveland still insisted that witnesses be interviewed separately.

By the time Lauren Tripp was sworn in, he had many things to clarify. But if the jury had asked previous witnesses about Lauren's character, it might have cast doubt over his testimony. According to Mapleton neighbors, Lauren had a reputation for fabricating stories. Most of his lies were harmless, meant to exaggerate his abilities and prowess. Lauren was what many would call a braggart.

The clean-shaven and smartly dressed 26-year-old took the stand. He was pressed about the many reports that he had been seen driving the canopied wagon the night of June 8th. Lauren admitted using the wagon that evening to search for Sarah. This, he explained, is why so many of his neighbors reported seeing the wagon in the vicinity that night. He also offered that he had resumed his search the next morning. When asked, Lauren told the jurors that he had even driven near where the body lay the following morning. But he claimed he had not seen Sarah's remains.

It is doubtful that Lauren's testimony deflected suspicion away from himself or his family. It did, however, point to the circumstantial nature of the evidence.

Henry Tripp took the stand for the second time. Only this time, it must have seemed to him, it was in his own defense. His grizzled appearance created a contrast to his son's fresh-faced youthfulness. His approach to the questioning was also distinctly different. What the younger Tripp explained, the elder flatly denied.

Cleveland asked about the canopied wagon that was seen heading towards the tracks on the night of Sarah's disappearance. Mr. Tripp adamantly denied that the rig had been used on the night in question. His testimony contradicted that of his son.

Cleveland asked a direct question about how the family treated Sarah. Tripp refuted allegations that he or his wife mistreated their adopted daughter. He admitted that he had punished Sarah in the past but never so severely as he had his own children.

Then the elder Tripp began to talk as Henry Tripp liked to do. He turned toward the jury and offered his version of what happened the night of June 8th. He repeated the theory that he had first told reporters about an abduction. Only this time, he added more details. He believed Sarah had been kidnapped and murdered by three young men of Pendleton; a story that sounded strangely similar to his daughter's "presentment."

Initially, he declined to name whom he suspected. But when pressed he named two Moyer boys and another boy named Bender as the culprits. His only reason for his suspicions was what he considered strange behavior when he spoke to one of the boys at Sarah's funeral. Tripp also testified that on several occasions he had seen the boys taunting the pretty girl by hollering "Hello, Sally" whenever they saw her.

Tripp's testimony created a stir. The coroner might have seen it as an attempt by Mr. Tripp to deflect suspicion away from his family. But Cleveland could not ignore an alternative theory. He had to remove any other possible explanation. As Sherlock Holmes said, "When you have eliminated the impossible, whatever remains, however improbable, must be the truth."

The jury, after some deliberation, was not yet able to come to a verdict. Cleveland told anxious reporters that when they did, it would likely be in the form of a sealed verdict handed directly to the District Attorney.

Once again, the inquest was adjourned. Cleveland scheduled what he hoped to be the final session for Saturday, July 15th.

27
Amelia

On Friday evening, the setting sun cast an orange light in the kitchen. Amelia stood next to her mother slicing salted pork for her father's supper while Ricca chopped vegetables. Neither turned around when her father opened the back door. They heard him hang his hat and settle up to the table like he did each night. Before her mother could ask if he washed, her father spoke.

"Got some bad news," he said. Ricca grabbed the plate of ham from Amelia and turned to set it on the table.

"Get on with it then," she said calmly.

"Heard that Tripp accused some boys of taking part in his girl's death." He said, getting right to the point. "Said one of them was Henry Bender."

Ricca sat down at the table. Amelia wondered if her mother hadn't heard him or if she was just letting the words settle in.

"Our Henry Bender?" Ricca asked.

Amelia's father nodded. He was not one to repeat himself.

"Involved how?" Amelia asked.

Her father looked at her mother to answer. "He claims they had indecent intentions toward the girl, and Tripp suspects they assaulted her," he said, "in a criminal way."

Ricca shifted uncomfortably. Amelia knew what was implied by "in a criminal" way.

"What proof does he have?" Ricca asked.

"Just the way he'd seen them act toward her; you know how boys are," he answered his wife.

"Well, I bet Mr. Tripp is just saying that to get people to stop suspecting him," Amelia said. She felt the defensiveness rise in her for her family. Her mother did not seem so affected by the news about her stepbrother.

"So, what's to come of them?" Ricca asked her husband as she set the rest of his supper in front of him.

He shrugged his shoulders. "They'll be called to answer to that inquest." He picked up his fork and began to eat his supper, signaling that he said all he knew.

Amelia sat at the table and stared across at her mother. She could see her hard lines fade and the worry began to show through. Her mother had worked diligently to keep scandal from darkening their family. This one she would not be able to contain.

Amelia's concern for her mother quickly shifted to Henry Bender. She thought about what he would have to face. To be accused of murder, or even worse, and to be questioned before an inquest sounded almost as terrifying as what she had been facing. Amelia had no way of knowing for sure if he had been involved or not. But she knew that if it came down to the word of a wealthy farmer and a poor farmhand, things might not look good for the farmhand.

28
Sarah's Story
July 15, 1899

Coroner Cleveland tried to keep the identity of the three boys from the press until he could rule them out as suspects. But holding an inquest behind closed doors did not keep witnesses from talking. Henry Tripp's accusation against the young men caused a stir in Pendleton. The town was small enough that most either knew the boys or their families.

Cleveland summoned the three adolescents to appear Saturday afternoon in Lockport. The inquest lasted into the evening.

Two of the boys that Henry Tripp accused were brothers. The Moyer brothers' parents tilled a small farm in Pendleton. Oscar, the younger of the two, was only 16. His older brother Albert was 18. The two worked together as farm hands across the town line in Cambria, just a few miles from the Tripp farm. The third boy, Henry Bender, was 17. He was a bit closer, working and living on a farm, just up the street from the Tripps.

Cleveland might have seen something of himself in the boy. Henry Bender had plenty in common with the coroner. Besides sharing a first name, both had lost their father at a tender age.

Henry Bender was the son of German immigrants. His parents came to this country when his mother Catherine was pregnant with Henry. He was born in the town of Lancaster less than thirty miles from Pendleton. But when he was less than a year old, his father died, leaving his mother alone to care for him. The young widow married a much older widowed farmer and moved to Pendleton. The widower, Frederick Burmeister, gave Henry his last name which he used most of his childhood. He grew up in Pendleton with a younger half-sister named Mary. But when he became old enough to decide for himself, he took the name of his deceased father.

The Burmeisters owned a small farm on Irish Road about five miles from the Tripp farm. But Henry lived just a couple houses away with the Miller family, the same family that had testified that Sarah had visited their home six weeks before her death.

Cleveland might have reminded the jurors of the timeline of the night of June 8th. Since the Tripps had reported her alive and well at 9:00 pm, and the train passed at midnight, the window for someone else to have taken her life and placed her on the tracks was less than three hours. Fortunately for the young men, they were all able to account for their whereabouts on the night of Sarah's disappearance. Friends and relatives stepped forward to provide alibis for the three boys accused by Mr. Tripp.

The jury seemed satisfied, at least for now, that the boys were not involved. But rumors still circulated that Sarah had been pregnant at the time of her death. Jurors might have wondered if one of the three boys could have been the father.

The jury deliberated for some time but was not able to reach a verdict.

Coroner Cleveland had presented plenty of testimony to dispel the original accounts of suicide. By this point in the inquest, the jury had heard testimony from over forty different witnesses. But Cleveland was persistent. It leaked to the press that a witness was issued a subpoena that day. The new witness–said to be a former classmate of one of Tripp's daughters–used to live at Lockport junction in Cambria. There must have been speculation as to whether this witness had anything to do with the closed-door testimony heard earlier in the week. Or was it something brought up that day by one of the boys or their alibi witnesses?

It might have been John B. Richardson. Richardson shocked the jury with a story that he had heard that Lauren had boasted about killing Sarah. He also told them that Lauren bragged about carrying a revolver. Lauren allegedly said that he might shoot someone if provoked. The testimony shed more light on Lauren's character, but it was still hearsay.

Cleveland knew that he needed hard evidence to remove any doubt, the kind that relied on science, not circumstance. After conferring with District Attorney Hopkins, he decided it was time to turn to Sarah Mumford to provide the answers they needed.

29
Amelia

On Sunday, Amelia waited anxiously for her parents to return from church. She hoped her mother had found a chance to speak to the Burmeisters and to ask about Henry's testimony at the inquest. The anticipation made it difficult to focus on the words in her bible. Sometimes her mother asked her about what she read, and Amelia did not want to give her more reasons to be aggravated with her. She thought maybe if she read to her unborn child, it would be easier.

She balanced her bible on her large belly and read out loud from the book of Genesis, "So, Rachel said to Jacob. 'Give me children or I will die!' Jacob became angry with Rachel and said, 'I am not God. He is the one who has caused you to not have children.' Then Rachel said, 'You can have my maid Bilhah. Sleep with her, and she will have a child for me. Then I can be a mother through her.'"

Amelia stopped. The story did not seem like a thing fit for a child to hear. Amelia heard her parents' voices outside. She closed the book.

As soon as her parents came through the door, Amelia started asking questions.

"Did you talk to Grandpa Burmeister?"

"I spoke to Catherine and Mary," Ricca answered.

"What did they say, did Henry testify?"

"He told them where he was that night," Ricca said. She tied her apron to begin preparing their meal. Amelia did the same.

"Did they believe him?" Amelia asked.

"There was someone to vouch for him," her mother said.

"Who?"

"I guess the family he stays with, the Millers." Said Ricca.

"So, does that mean he won't be arrested? What did the other boys say?" Amelia's questions were coming faster than her mother could think.

"Amelia, stop." Ricca raised her voice and put up her hand. "I was not there."

Amelia took a long breath. She felt her heart pounding rapidly.

"Sit," her mother commanded. Amelia sat at the table. She felt like crying but could not name the source of her distress.

Ricca went back to preparing the meal.

Amelia wished she had inherited her mother's fortitude. She had never been as stoic, but lately, she felt her emotions were like a powerful current held back by a paper wall. And they were all jumbled up so she could not always tell where they were coming from.

She had been worried that Henry might be arrested if things didn't go well at the inquest. But Henry Bender would not be the first of her family to spend some time behind bars. Uncle Fritz had the honor of that distinction. And if Amelia was perfectly honest with herself, she felt some relief to have someone help carry the family's burden of shame. Even if just for a while. But still, she did not want to see Henry imprisoned, if he was falsely accused.

Maybe it was because confined to their home, she felt like she was imprisoned. The baby would arrive by the end of the month. She had been counting the days down like a prisoner waiting for a pardon. But now that the time had neared, she realized that her pardon might never come.

30
Sarah's Story
July 17, 1899

Henry Tripp now claimed he was convinced that Sarah was murdered and was anxious for the murderers to be discovered. More than forty witnesses testified since the start of the inquest, which had begun a month before. But most of the evidence against the Tripps was still circumstantial.

The jurors believed that they were dealing with a homicide. The evidence pointed to the 'what' of their investigation being a murder rather than an accident or suicide. The task at hand was to determine who was responsible. The issue of motive seemed to be a cloudy one. If they only knew why Sarah was murdered, they might find their answer.

Cleveland considered the possibilities. There were a few theories circulated as to the motive of this crime. Thus far, he attempted to gather evidence to prove these theories. But Pettit's preliminary examination of the body, as it turned out, was not a thorough one. He was unable to refute the claims put forth. Sherlock Holmes would focus on eliminating all possibilities until only one remained. Cleveland knew of one way to do this.

On Monday morning, Coroner Cleveland directed that the body of Sarah Mumford be exhumed. A small party proceeded to the Shawnee cemetery. A mound of dirt still covered the five-week-old grave. The digger's spade easily parted the loose soil to unearth the wooden coffin.

The remains were examined by Doctor Loomis, who led the autopsy.

Loomis hailed from Oswego County, about 150 miles west. He had moved to Lockport ten years prior and had already gained a reputation as a skilled physician. Cleveland trusted him with his own medical care, even though Loomis was a loyal Republican. The pair had adjoining offices on Main Street. Loomis lived on Waterman Street with his wife and child, just a few houses from Cleveland. His daughter was the same age as Sarah Mumford.

Dr. Pettit assisted Loomis in the autopsy. The two physicians were opposites in politics and the practice of medicine. Dr. Loomis, an allopath, subscribed to an orthodox discipline of medical practice. This contrasted with Dr. Pettit's homeopathic background. This non-conventional practice of medicine was shunned by the American Medical Association for most of the nineteenth century. Unorthodox or not, homeopathic doctors remained a popular choice of patients. But how Loomis and Pettit went about treating their patients did not matter. The body examined had been dead for nearly five weeks.

This was not the first time Cleveland had a body exhumed because the coroner suspected foul play. In 1892, Cleveland received word about a death that occurred in his county shrouded in what he believed to be suspicious circumstances. An elderly and childless woman, living alone in Olcott, had died suddenly. Her relatives arranged for the justice of the peace to hold an informal inquest without notifying the coroner. Since a doctor present gave the opinion that she must have died of heart failure, the cause of death was listed as such.

That he had not been notified of the death and informal inquest incensed Cleveland. The relatives stood to inherit an estate worth more than $12,000. All of this caused the coroner great suspicion. He ordered the body exhumed, and he impaneled a jury. He enlisted Dr. Pettit to perform an autopsy.

Dr. Pettit examined the Olcott woman's heart and found it to be in good condition. An examination of her other major organs proved the same. According to Pettit, she had been in perfect health, her death notwithstanding. Determined to find the cause of death, he brought the stomach back to Lockport to examine its contents for poison.

Word of the new inquest had caught the attention of the newsmen. Cleveland tried to keep a tight lid on the case until the jurors heard the evidence. Nonetheless, the *Buffalo Courier* printed an article before the scheduled inquest with a leaked story that suffocation was suspected based on the doctor's findings. "A report prevails that the blood in the body was in a peculiar state of fluidity, with its solid and coloring matter deposited, which usually results from asphyxiation." The journalist wrote his interpretation of what he heard to be Dr. Pettit's analysis.

In 1892, forensic medicine was not a fully formed and accepted science. Though the century saw many scientific advancements, no formal forensic training existed. Even if Pettit had found evidence indicating suffocation, it most likely would not have been understood by the jurors. Cleveland poked around Olcott trying to find more evidence to support the doctor's suspicion. In the end, nothing came of the inquest.

Not everyone had appreciated the innuendos of foul play and the coroner's actions in the 1892 case. In a letter to the editor of the *Lockport Sun,* a concerned citizen voiced their distress. "The deceased ought to have been left to remain in her grave and without a second inquisition being held, the carving and mutilating following of course."

Past failure and criticism did not dissuade the coroner. He determined that exhuming the body was essential to the present case. Cleveland hoped the autopsy of Sarah Mumford would prove to be the evidence needed to solve the mystery of her death.

31
Amelia

Amelia rose early. She had spent most of the night staring at the ceiling and thinking about the inquest. Despite the lack of sleep, she felt fueled with a sort of nervous energy.

She went to the kitchen. Both of her parents stood at the back door. Her mother handed her father a baked potato for his lunch. He shoved the potato into his pocket and left without so much as a goodbye.

"I can gather the eggs," Amelia offered.

Her mother shook her head. "I'll do it." Ricca had not let Amelia gather eggs or haul water since her stomach swelled. Amelia thought it was not the heavy lifting that concerned her mother so much as the chance of being spotted by a nosey neighbor.

"You can sift the ashes if you're looking for something to start on," Ricca said as she followed out the door.

Amelia started toward the iron stove and noticed the newspaper with the article about Sarah Mumford. She had been trying to piece together a timeline in her head for the night she went missing. She concluded that there were a few people who might have had an opportunity to harm Sarah that night.

When her mother came back into the house with an apron full of eggs, Amelia was sitting at the stove holding the paper and staring off.

“What are you doing?” her mother asked, with an edge of annoyance.

“I have been thinking about how many motives there might be to commit a murder,” said Amelia. Ricca sighed loudly. She shook her head and placed the eggs in a basket. Without a word, she grabbed the water bucket and went back outside, closing the door harder than needed.

Anger, Amelia thought, might push someone to kill. She pondered a little longer. Jealousy was the motive for Cain killing Abel. She decided revenge might also be a motive for murder, but she could not think of anything Sarah might have done to deserve revenge. Amelia recalled another story she once read about someone killing for money and thought that greed should be added to the list. But what would anyone have to gain by killing Sarah Mumford? Another motive, Amelia thought, could be to hide something or keep someone from sharing a secret. She wished she had a pencil to make a list. Then she remembered one more.

Her mother came back through the door carrying a bucket of water.

“Maybe Mr. Tripp is right. Maybe Sarah was killed by someone with indecent intentions,” Amelia said.

“Amelia!” her mother spoke her name sharply as a warning. Amelia knew young girls did not speak of such things. But too much had passed for her mother to pretend she was still an innocent child. Amelia knew too well the ways of some men.

“Isn’t it strange how there is no mention of Lauren Tripp’s wife?”

Ricca did not respond. She poured the water into a larger basin.

"Maybe she saw something that made her jealous," Amelia continued.

Ricca slammed the empty bucket to the floor. She turned toward Amelia, her face red with anger. "It's wrong to speculate this way, about things you know nothing about," her mother chastised. "You do not know what it is like to live in that woman's shoes."

Amelia froze. Her mother's reprimand stung, and she could feel tears start to build behind her eyes.

"Don't you start crying like a child," Ricca scolded. The anger in her mother's voice made it hard to hold back the tears. Amelia could feel her throat begin to swell. She bit her trembling lip.

"You are not a child." Ricca shook her finger. "You are a grown woman with grown woman problems, and it is time you face them instead of worrying about other people." Ricca paused. "I cannot protect you from everything."

Amelia thought she saw a small tear in her mother's eyes. Her own tears poured down her cheeks, unable to be contained. Amelia threw her head in her hands and sobbed. A dam of emotion had burst, and she could only gulp for air.

As she tried to wipe away the tears, Amelia heard her mother walk out the door and close it behind her.

32
Sarah's Story
July 18, 1899

Tuesday started hot; by noon temperatures reached the mid-eighties. But the lake-fueled humidity made it feel much hotter. It was set to be the last day of the inquest. The jury and most everyone in Niagara County anxiously awaited the results of the autopsy.

Before he entered the witness room, a reporter asked Dr. Wilson Pettit if after five weeks it was still possible to determine certain conditions of the deceased at the time of her death.

He replied that he and Dr. Loomis had found out what the jury had wanted to know.

The jurors listened intently as Abner Loomis was sworn in. Dr. Loomis testified that he had found several wounds on the body sufficient to be a cause of death. It was revealed that Sarah had a fractured skull. This and other wounds, Loomis reported, were sufficient to have caused her death.

He went on to testify that her wounds, including the skull fracture, would have caused external hemorrhaging of an excessive amount. That no blood was found on the body or in the vicinity made it clear that she had already been dead before the train struck her.

When asked about the cause of death, Dr. Loomis was unable to provide such certainty. Because of the number of injuries, and the damage done by the train, it was impossible to determine the exact cause of death.

Next, jurors would hear the testimony of Dr. Pettit. The notably handsome physician took the stand. His prominent mustache drew attention to his words.

Not only did he assist Dr. Loomis in the delayed autopsy, but Pettit was the physician who made the initial postmortem examination on June 9th. He noted the testimony of those at the scene of the accident and offered his professional analysis. Corpses do not bleed, he explained. Had she been alive when struck by the train, blood would have splattered across the track.

The testimony of both physicians confirmed a principal element of this case for the jurors. Sarah died in a different location and then was placed on the tracks.

But there was more to be clarified. Dr. Pettit had conducted the initial examination of Sarah when her body was first discovered. He testified that he found no evidence that Sarah had been sexually assaulted. In the minds of the coroner's jury, this testimony further exonerated the young men fingered by Henry Tripp.

The conclusion that Sarah had not been criminally assaulted probably was not based on the autopsy. Her pelvis had been crushed. More likely Pettit's opinion came from the lack of evidence found in the original postmortem examination. Perhaps he found no signs of a struggle, no trace evidence left under fingernails, no bruising, not obviously caused by the train. But it was unclear how thorough Pettit's original examination had been. He would not have been looking for signs of a struggle. Train fatalities usually proved to be accidents or suicides. It was not yet recognized as a means to conceal a crime of a different nature.

There was one more rumor that both Cleveland and his panel wanted to either squelch or confirm. As promised, Dr. Pettit had an answer. According to the autopsy, there was no evidence that Sarah Mumford was pregnant at the time of her murder. This might have shocked the jury who had heard testimony to the contrary.

To Cleveland, the medical testimony provided jurors with the clarifications needed. But after the physicians had testified, Cleveland wanted the jurors to hear one more piece of evidence. He summoned Lauren Tripp to be reexamined based on an unusual tip he had received. Cleveland's line of questions might have taken the jurors by surprise. But he believed it added another link stringing the Tripp family to the crime.

There were still more witnesses he wanted to hear from. But with clear evidence that a crime had been committed, and many rumors dispelled, he hoped the jury could reach a conclusion. He had already notified the District Attorney that something would be coming his way.

33
Amelia

Amelia could not remember a hotter July. Or maybe it just felt that way. The humidity filled their house like a Dutch oven, trapped inside with no place to go. The baby pushed against her lower gut like it had started to squirm its way toward an escape.

Amelia and her mother had not spoken since yesterday morning. Nothing had changed between her father and her. He still avoided looking directly at her whenever possible. Lately, she barely saw him at all. He left the house before she woke and only came in to eat. The last few evenings he retreated to the shed as soon as he finished his supper.

Despite the heat, Amelia could not sit still. Since there was no comfortable position, she busied herself with as many chores as she could find. There was always plenty to do, and she discovered she did not need to wait for Ricca to ask. Amelia rubbed the kitchen windows with a vinegar-soaked rag. The smell made her nauseous, but they needed to be done. Maybe if her mother found her useful, she would have more reason to keep her around. She had already lost one parent's affection; she did not think she could afford to lose the other.

34
Sarah's Story
July 19, 1899

On Wednesday morning, the Tripps began their day as usual. Both Henry and Lauren rose early to tend the fields. Iva kept her mother company and tried to soothe her worries as best she could. Try as they may, this was no ordinary day. The family awaited the verdict which would set the course for the near future and possibly the rest of their lives.

If the coroner's jury ruled no evidence against them, vindication would be the order of the day. Iva would surely revel in the idea of putting her gossipy neighbors and ill-sayers in their place. But it was the other outcome that Matilda was dreading. The jury had the power to issue an indictment and charge one of her family members with the murder of Sarah Mumford.

After five weeks of deliberation the coroner's jury had reached their decision, the verdict not yet known to the Tripp Family.

Shortly after noon, as they were clearing the table from the midday meal, they heard a knock. Iva opened the front door to the first of two unexpected visitors they would receive that day. A reporter from the *Buffalo Times* stood at the doorway, looking for a new angle on his next article. Iva introduced herself and her mother. Mrs. Tripp did little to hide the trepidation wrinkled across her brow.

Iva led the reporter to the stubble field. They found Henry Tripp maneuvering the horse-drawn rake when he spotted the two walking toward him. The farmer interrupted his work to talk to the journalist about the latest development in the inquest.

Mr. Tripp explained that he and his family had given their testimony earlier, and he had little more to add. The reporter then asked him if his view of what happened to Sarah Mumford had changed considering the autopsy. Tripp hesitated, then offered his reply.

"It was my theory that Sarah had been abducted and after being criminally assaulted, had been murdered. Then her remains had been placed on the track in the hope that a passing train would destroy all evidence of the foul crime that I believe had been perpetrated," Tripp told the reporter. "A postmortem examination, however, upset that theory as it proved that Sarah had not lost her virginity. Now I am all at sea. I know nothing more today than I did the hour she left."

Dr. Pettit had testified that there was no evidence of a sexual assault. That Sarah had been a virgin was Henry Tripp's interpretation.

"I know of no reason, whatever, why she should have left or how she came to be where she was found," Mr. Tripp said.

Iva listened intently as her father spoke. "If we only knew," she added. "If we only knew."

Lauren approached the conversation and introduced himself but allowed his father to do the speaking.

"There is no truth in the stories that she had been misused. She had not been punished in a year and a half. Sarah had got along to that age so that she was of considerable help in the household," the elder Tripp said.

The newsman probed for more information about the mysterious Sarah Mumford.

"She had been an inmate of my family for several years, being taken from an orphanage in Rochester when a small child." Mr. Tripp explained that the family knew little about Sarah's background. He believed Sarah's father had died due to his own intemperance.

The reporter stayed no more than an hour. He left before the second unexpected caller of the day came to the Tripp home. This time it was Ira Baker, the Pendleton Constable. In his hand, he held four warrants.

Earlier that day, at eleven a.m., the coroner's jury handed their verdict to District Attorney Hopkins.

"That said Sarah A. Mumford met her death on June 8th at the hands of Henry Tripp, Matilda Tripp, or [Lauren] Tripp and that Iva Tripp was an accessory to the crime: and further, that they be held and examined before a magistrate, according to the law." Jurors James Shaw, Edward Manning, George W. Pencille, Oliver Longmate, Frank A. Harmony, Charles P. Hemmer, Frank Watt, and James Nelson all signed the indictment.

Constable Baker made the arrests at the home of the Tripps at three p.m. He transported all four to Lockport.

The Niagara County jailhouse, sculpted in red brick, stood three and a half stories high. A dozen steps ascended into a wide archway like a drawbridge over a castle moat. The four Tripps climbed the stairs. Henry Tripp and his two adult children held their composure. Whether it was shock, righteousness, or an instinct to conceal their emotion, their demeanor revealed nothing but stoicism. Mrs. Tripp was a different story. Upon hearing the news of her impending arrest, she collapsed into hysteria. The assurance of her husband and children was not sufficient to contain her grief. She struggled to stand on her own as she walked up the stairs.

The county judge, who would normally preside over the arraignment, was unavailable. A recent law placed the coroner as the acting magistrate in his absence. So, it befell Cleveland to set bail for the prisoners. Given the gravity of the charges, he issued a $12,000 bond, $3000 for each one of the Tripps.

$12,000 amounted to a small fortune in 1899. But Tripp had financial resources. He was able to arrange for the full amount by the end of the afternoon. However, Cleveland would not allow Mr. Tripp to sign for himself. Eventually, he permitted Tripp to secure his wife and daughter's bond so the women would not spend the night in jail. But Cleveland insisted the Tripp men find another party to secure the remaining amount.

Constable Baker escorted the elder Tripp around Pendleton as he attempted to find someone to secure his bond. As the hour grew later and no one was found, Henry Tripp gave up. Constable Baker returned him to the jail and allowed Lauren a chance to seek out someone willing to post the bond. He, too, was unsuccessful.

A worn Matilda signed the release, eager to return home. Iva also showed the strain of the day in her bloated eyes. However, she mustered a last bit of defiance. The bond agreement listed her name as Ivy Tripp, and she refused to sign as such. Her name, she contended, was Iva E. Tripp.

District Attorney Abner Hopkins instructed her to sign it, insomuch as she had been referred to as Ivy throughout the inquest. Iva retorted that if the coroner's jury wished to charge Ivy Tripp, then they had the wrong person.

Hopkins pointed out to her that Cleveland's decision to release her on bond was not required and that she should be grateful.

"I do not see anything to be grateful for in this miserable proceeding against our family," Iva said indignantly. Hopkins blushed at the spirited interchange. Then he reminded Iva if she did not sign, she would spend the night in jail.

"But I do not see that I need a bond, for apparently, you've arrested the wrong party," she said as she signed Ivy Tripp. "That is not my name."

That Wednesday evening both Iva and Matilda returned to their home with the promise to come back the next day for arraignment. Henry and Lauren spent the night in the Niagara County jail. The two occupied adjoining seven-by-ten cells. Located on the ground floor, their accommodations included a wash bowl, a small sanitary closet, and the occasional rodent.

35
Amelia

Amelia scrubbed the hem of a skirt with a small brush. Her nose filled with the smell of vinegar and soap. Her father had walked to Pendleton Center right after supper. Amelia felt sure it was to avoid sitting in the same house with his undeniably shamed and unmarried daughter. She wobbled so much when she walked, it seemed like she announced her condition whenever she entered a room.

Ricca stood over the kitchen table sorting clothes in preparation for tomorrow's wash. They both heard him lumber up the back steps before the door opened.

"They arrested the Tripp Family," her father announced just as soon as he stepped inside. Amelia's mother tossed a blue striped shirt onto the pile.

"The whole family?" Ricca asked.

"Just about," he replied.

Amelia listened in, afraid to say anything for fear it would trigger another scolding from her mother.

"What are they charged with?" Ricca sounded somewhat surprised by the news.

"Murder," he answered. Amelia's father hung up his hat and sat down at the table.

"How could they all have murdered her?" Ricca asked. Amelia's father took a seat. "What proof do they have? Seems to me it's all just gossip," Ricca said.

Amelia wondered what the inquest had found. She reasoned it must be hard evidence or at least explain why they would want her dead.

"Coroner must think he has a good case to be arresting a family like the Tripps," Amelia's father said. Ricca nodded in agreement.

"There will be a trial," Ricca said, "That should give the town plenty to talk about for the rest of the summer."

It pleased Amelia to learn that someone was standing up for Sarah. But she agreed with her mother, they did not all do it. *Which one could it be? And why?*

She scrubbed harder at the stained hem while she pondered it over. The stubborn stain clung to the fabric.

Amelia had come to believe that the Tripp family had hidden Sarah to conceal how they treated her. But the only ones they silenced were their neighbors, the people who were too afraid to speak out until it was too late. Maybe Sarah threatened to speak out about it. Either way, she was sure Sarah had been brave. *I could use some of Sarah's courage.*

36
Sarah's Story
July 20, 1899

The next day, both Henry and Lauren Tripp lay stretched on their cots in the county jail. when an eager reporter paid them a visit, hoping for another quote. Their lawyers had instructed them to cease engagement with the press. Lauren took the advice of his attorney. Henry Tripp tried to restrain himself.

"I won't do any talking now," he told the reporter. "Our turn's to come yet, and when other people get through, we will have something to say."

No response was needed to get the old man to continue.

"This case is not over yet," Tripp said. "I'm sorry to disoblige you, but there is really nothing to the whole business, except that some folks who are talking now will be sorry later on."

The jailer came by and asked the men if they would like a meal.

"Yes," said Lauren, "if you have anything to eat." He likely had not eaten since the previous day.

"I'll give you beans," the jailer said, "bean soup and not very good at that."

Lauren wrinkled his face and shook his head in disgust.

"No, we'll get something in town pretty soon," his father said. "We'll be out of this before long."

The jailer went on leaving the two without their fill. It was four more hours before they received word that bail had been arranged.

Henry V. Meahl and Tony Moyer, no relation to the brothers accused by Henry Tripp, posted the bonds. Both were established farmers in the area. Meahl's motives, at least, were not entirely neighborly. The prosperous farmer had the elder Tripp give him a mortgage on his farmland for the bond. Meahl claimed he needed security in case the Tripp men failed to show up to court. To Mr. Tripp, it might have seemed like his neighbor was capitalizing on his misfortune.

At four p.m. Matilda and Iva returned as promised. The four Tripps stood before Cleveland, still acting as a magistrate, to answer the charges. Henry Tripp's wealth afforded him an enviable defense team. Attorneys W. Luther Reeves, a Lockport justice of the peace, and Daniel E. Brong, the former District Attorney, represented the family.

Lockport District Attorney Abner T. Hopkins was out of the city on other business. In his place, Assistant District Attorney Bert G. Stockwell appeared for the people.

Reeves spoke first for the defense. The young attorney stood to speak and moved that the case be dismissed. He asserted that no evidence had been produced at the inquest determining the manner of death. Reeves conceded that the autopsy results indicated that Sarah was not killed by the train. But it also pointed to a death resulting in a large amount of blood, the lawyer noted. He went on to emphasize that no evidence of blood stain had yet to be obtained from the Tripp property. Therefore, he motioned that the case be dismissed due to the lack of evidence connecting the defendants to the crime.

Reeves, like most people, assumed that the lack of blood splatter meant Sarah bled out somewhere else. The absence of blood on the scene indicated that Sarah's heart had not been pumping blood when the train hit her. Whatever the cause of death, when her heart stopped, blood pressure immediately ceased. Soon after her death, her blood would have settled due to a process called livor mortis. Over time, her blood would have become fixed. This meant Sarah's death might have come from something other than one of the injuries revealed by the autopsy. But Medical Examiners of the time, let alone defense attorneys, did not fully understand livor mortis.

To Reeves' point, no immediate search of the Tripp property had been conducted. Cleveland probably regretted Dr. Pettit's original assumption that Sarah had been killed by the railroad cars. It prevented the gathering of evidence at any potential crime scene. The notion of using trace evidence to solve crimes was more common in detective stories than in actual criminal investigations. But Dr. Pettit had used a microscope to solve crimes before. He had once been called on to examine a substance found on a possible murder weapon as blood. His testimony helped to convict a man. But even if Cleveland had found blood at the Tripp farm, Mr. Tripp could have claimed it came from a slaughtered pig like he told Willis Olds. It was another two years before a young German doctor, Paul Uhlenhuth, developed a test to distinguish human blood from animals.

Assistant District Attorney Stockwell responded to the defense, armed with a mountain of testimony from the thorough inquest. He pointed to the evidence that the Tripp wagon had been seen by more than one witness heading towards the tracks where Sarah's murdered body was found.

As acting magistrate, Cleveland was not going to allow the case he had worked so diligently to build to be dismissed so easily. At the defense's request, a preliminary hearing in the case of the people versus Henry, Matilda, Lauren, and Ida Tripp was set for the following week in Lockport.

The purpose of the hearing was to determine if the case had enough merit to go to trial. To do so, the prosecution had to present evidence that a crime had been committed and evidence that the defendants were involved. In preparation, the District Attorney directed the court stenographer to type up the coroner's report for the defense.

The Tripp family, having all posted bail, went home to await the hearing. Lauren ate his supper as soon as he arrived home that evening. Afterward, he walked to the post office at Mapleton Station, whistling loudly along the way. According to neighbors, he seemed to enjoy the notoriety his arrest had provided him.

37
Amelia
July 25, 1899

Amelia opened her heavy eyelids and tried to lift her head. Exhausted, she laid it back on the pillow and closed her eyes again. The last thing she remembered was her mother placing the baby on her chest to feed. *The baby, where is my baby?*

She opened her eyes again and tried to focus on the objects around her. She heard a tiny cry. The doctor was standing near her.

"Where's my baby?" she said, her voice hoarse from the screams of labor. Her mother placed a hand on her shoulder. She had been standing at her bedside all along. It was Ricca, not the doctor that did most of the delivery. The doctor arrived when it was almost over.

"Dr. Helwig is checking her over," Amelia's mother said. Amelia looked at the doctor as he examined the infant. She recognized him. It was the same doctor who had come the night her sister Rachael had died four years earlier.

Dr. Helwig handed the baby back to Ricca.

"She looks healthy," he said.

Ricca swaddled the baby and placed her back in Amelia's arms. Amelia felt a wave of relief. She had been so afraid. Afraid of the pain, afraid of what would happen to her, but it had not occurred to her to be afraid for the baby, until now.

Dr. Helwig placed his stethoscope back in his leather satchel and pulled out a pencil and a dark green notebook. He sat down in a chair next to the bed and jotted a few things in the book.

"What will the child's name be?" he asked.

"Maud," Amelia answered. "Maud Amanda."

The doctor scribbled the name. Amelia looked down at her daughter. She was so small, so helpless. It was her job to protect her. She thought about what her mother said about facing her problems. She looked at Dr. Helwig. He closed his book and held it in his hand.

"And the father's name is Owen Ryan," she said.

"I did not think there was a husband?" Dr. Helwig looked directly at Ricca.

"He's not my husband, but he is the baby's father," Amelia said. Her voice regained some of its strength.

"I am afraid it's not customary to record the father's name when there's no marriage unless he is here to vouch for the child," Helwig said.

"My daughter can vouch he is the father," Ricca interjected. "Promises were made."

Dr. Helwig turned back to Amelia.

"You're sure?" he asked.

Amelia ignored the insult. *Why should Owen get a choice when she has none.*

"I'm sure," she said. Her jaw stiffened. "Owen Ryan, he lives in Lockport, and he knows he is the father." Owen would be furious, but Amelia refused to hide his secret any longer. He was older than her and had a good job in a paper mill. Maud was the one who needed protection.

“If you put his name in the book,” Ricca said, “he will have to be responsible.”

Helwig hesitated as if he was considering what to do. He looked at each of the women and then rested his eyes on the small child.

“It won’t force him to do anything,” he said, “but I suppose it might help.” Slowly, he reopened the book and wrote down the name.

Ricca nodded her head at Amelia. She seemed pleased. Helwig stood to leave. Ricca thanked the Doctor and walked with him to the door. Before he left the room, he turned back to Amelia.

“You’re a brave girl,” Helwig said, “like your mother.”

Amelia looked at her mother and then at Maud. She did not feel brave. She felt tired and terrified. She didn’t know what would happen and she did not think she could do it alone.

Ricca came back into the room with Amelia’s father following behind her. In his arms, he carried a wooden cradle. Amelia could smell the freshly cut wood.

“For the baby,” he said. Her father placed the cradle next to Amelia’s bed. He rubbed his calloused hands over the wood. “It’s sturdy, made it myself.”

Amelia could feel the tears filling her eyes. “It’s lovely, Papa,’ she whispered, “Danka.”

Henry nodded and left the room.

Amelia looked up at her mother.

“You should try to feed the baby and then try to sleep some more,” Ricca said. She moved to the bedside to help her daughter.

“I thought he hated me.”

Ricca shook her head. “Heartbroken, yes, but still your Papa.”

Ricca placed her hand on the baby’s head and then moved it to her daughter’s. She brushed back some hair from Amelia’s face. “Someday, Amelia,” she said, “you’ll learn to see through other people’s eyes.”

38
Sarah's Story
July 26, 1899

The investigation of Sarah Mumford's death had been the talk of the town of Pendleton all summer. The sensational story had been picked up by local papers in Lockport, Niagara Falls, and Buffalo. Early articles simply referred to Sarah as a 16-year-old servant girl. When the press learned she was the adopted daughter of a prominent family, their interest peaked. When the Tripp family became suspects, the story became about them. And when the news hit the wire that four members of the Tripp family had been arrested, it became a front-page story across the Northeast. The *New York Times* printed a detailed story including an artist's rendition of Miss Sarah Mumford.

An enterprising reporter from the *North Tonawanda Argus* caught the Tripp family at home only a few days after their release on bail.

Iva Tripp answered the knock and let the reporter in. Matilda sat paring apples in a corner chair, her face still terror-stricken from her arrest. Henry came in from the fields. The reporter asked him to share his story, and the old farmer looked eager to talk. But just as he opened his mouth to speak, Iva interrupted.

"Remember what the lawyer said," she reminded him, and that ended the interview.

The journalist left the Tripp home and canvassed the neighborhood. He reported that he talked to many people but found no one claiming to be a friend to the Tripp family in a mile radius.

The *Niagara Falls Gazette* published a lure, sent by the *Syracuse Herald,* for a full story of the tragic death of Sarah Mumford. The *Herald* had dispatched a reporter 150 miles to gain photos and interviews from those involved in the case. As promised, the Syracuse paper printed a two-page spread in their Sunday edition including several photos and sketches of the major people and places involved in the case. The reporter, who had talked to neighbors, noted a pervasive sentiment that the Tripp family was somehow responsible.

A popular opinion among the neighbors was that Sarah had been beaten to death by Henry Tripp and that her death had been more accidental than premeditated. Most also believed that the Tripps placed the body on the tracks to cover the death and avert any suspicion or scandal.

Not all were set against the Tripps. There were some words of condolence conveyed to the family. Some might have argued that people were just jealous of Henry Tripp's prosperity. Or, that past quarrels had biased folks against the Tripps. It was true that the Tripp family had made enemies long before the inquest. Even Henry Tripp's brother had not spoken to him in years.

The *Buffalo Evening Times* ran their piece containing the interview of the family at their home the morning of their arrests. The article posed the Tripp family in a sympathetic light. It described Lauren as the picture of innocence:

"If ever a man's countenance betokened innocence of crime, in deed or intent, then this young man is guiltless of the awful charges that rests against him."

As for Henry Tripp, the *Times* representative asserted that the only thing "that could possibly be urged against him was that he had been more successful in acquiring property than the bulk of residents in his locality. In the eyes of some, this is regarded as a cardinal sin. It seems to be in his case."

There might have been some basis for the reporter's opinion. The town of Pendleton held two populations of residents. Most prominent families, like the Tripps, had been established since the town's beginnings in the early eighteen hundreds. They had already accumulated large tracts of land by midcentury when a surge of German immigrants came to settle. The Germans proved themselves to be good neighbors and industrious farmers. Most purchased a few acres sufficient to sustain their own families. They formed their own German-speaking congregations, and the two communities happily lived side by side.

But by the 1880s, the second industrial revolution had widened the gap between the small subsistence farms and the bigger farmers. Large farms could take advantage of modernized equipment and better transportation. But smaller farms struggled.

It was not uncommon for a family to have to send their children to live as hired hands or house servants for their well-to-do neighbors.

When a farm faced foreclosure, some already prosperous farmers saw it as an opportunity to capitalize on their neighbor's misfortune. Or at least that is how it might have felt to the less fortunate farmer.

In particular, the testimony of Lorenzo LeValley might have been tainted with an old resentment. When he told the jury that Henry and Lauren Tripp assaulted an elderly neighbor, he might not have told the whole story. The incident happened in 1898.

LeValley owned a small farm adjacent to the Tripp farm. The sheriff had sold the property, the fate of farmers who could not pay their debts. Henry Tripp secured the property for his son Lauren. Mr. LeValley, with the help of his father-in-law, Daniel Dieffenbacher, was removing the last of his possessions. When Dieffenbacher pulled his wagon onto the property, Henry Tripp confronted the old man. Before he could respond, he alleged that Lauren Tripp lunged at him and knocked him to the ground. The 86-year-old man suffered great pain and required a physician. The family filed a complaint and charged Lauren with second-degree assault.

Henry Tripp wrote a lengthy letter to the *Lockport Daily Journal* defending his son. Tripp stated that the confrontation began earlier in the day when he saw Mrs. Dieffenbacher removing property that he believed belonged to the farm. When he saw Mr. Dieffenbacher return to the property in the wagon, Tripp took it upon himself to order him off the premises. He reported that Dieffenbacher threatened him with a pitchfork before he left, and then he later returned. Tripp again ordered them to leave, and a confrontation ensued. Tripp described the account in his letter, referring to himself in the third person:

> He persisted in saying he had as much right there as anyone, and again raised his fork, this time to let it fall heavily on the head of Mr.

> Tripp who recovered himself and wrenched the fork from him, throwing it some distance. After Mr. Dieffenbacber had struck this blow, Lauren Tripp, son of Henry Tripp, pushed Mr. Dieffenbacher from his father but did not strike him, nor was he at any time thrown to the ground.
>
> Mr. Tripp then attempted to get into Mr. Dieffenbacher's wagon in order to drive the team into the road when Mr. LeValley grabbed him by the arm and back, and his son Marvin LeValley stood just above them on a load of hay brandishing a pitchfork and saying, 'Someone will get hurt.' But neither Mr. Tripp nor his son had a weapon of any kind. Just at this moment, there was another arrival on the scene and matters soon quieted down.

The incident resulted in assault charges against Lauren. The case went before the grand jury. But the jury returned a finding of 'no bill' and the matter was dropped.

Residents of Pendleton began to wonder if the case against the Tripp Family for Sarah Mumford's murder would yield the same verdict. They would have to wait to find out. The widely anticipated start of the preliminary hearing was delayed. Tripp's defense attorney, Daniel E. Brong, asked for a three-week extension to examine the evidence presented at the coroner's inquest.

District Attorney Hopkins told reporters that he could not push for the hearing to resume any sooner. It seemed that the report from the coroner's inquest amounted to 300 typewritten pages. The stenographer would later submit a bill to the county for $165 for his services on the case. The lengthy report included the examination of forty-eight witnesses. The defense now had the names and testimony of everyone who spoke out against the Tripps.

The preliminary examination was postponed until August 18th.

39
Amelia

Amelia lifted baby Maud from her cradle and laid her on the bed. The baby squeaked and squirmed until Amelia rewrapped her in a tight swaddle.

"There you go, Maud, that's better." She lifted the child over her shoulder and sat down on the bed. Amelia felt another wave coming. She held the child tightly as the feeling swept through her body like she was being pulled down into a pit. Amelia breathed slowly to steady her heart.

"It's okay, Maud, we're going to be alright," she said more to soothe herself than her child.

Amelia lowered the infant in her arms and pushed the blanket to the side to get a better look at the baby's round face. Maud reminded her of a porcelain doll she had seen in a store, only prettier.

"Your eyes are the color of the lake," she told the baby. She hummed a lullaby, and Maud stared up at her young mother. This made Amelia smile. "Your mama's right here." Her thoughts shifted to the babies that did not have mamas; the ones in the orphanage crying for someone to love them. She thought of Sarah, who was taken from her mother and had no one to watch out for her. She wondered if Sarah and her mother cried for each other the night she died.

Amelia knew that it was her mother that stood between herself and the cruel reality of her fate. She vowed to do the same for her child.

"You'll always have a family who loves you," she whispered in Maud's tiny ear. "I promise."

40

Sarah's Story

August 11, 1899

The Tripp family awaited their hearing from the comfort of their own home. Henry and Matilda Tripp resumed their lives as best as possible, as did Lauren and Iva. Work still needed to be done so the family passed the time as normally as possible. But everything was hardly normal. The grave charges and potential outcome if taken to trial must have loomed over them. To present in public without the stares of curious onlookers was nearly impossible. Even their closest neighbors seemed in league against them.

The Friday edition of the *Buffalo Times* reported on the anticipated pending trial and the impact on the town of Pendleton and the otherwise quiet village of Mapleton.

"Every social gathering at Mapleton, Niagara County considers one topic, the question of guilt or innocence of the Tripp family, charged with murder of the late Sarah Mumford. The known circumstances connected with this young girl's taking off are rehearsed almost daily. If the crime is not finally brought home to the Tripps, a fine crop of suits for slander will follow."

Savvy journalists found ways to continue to capitalize on the story. Since the inquest called on almost fifty witnesses, there was a lot of information to report. Some journalists added their own sensationalized spin to the story. Most chose to report the same pertinent facts: the testimony of the rail workers showing no blood on the tracks; the witnesses' descriptions of Sarah's abuse at the hands of the Tripp family; the report of the canopy wagon near the tracks where her lifeless body was discovered; and the testimony of the physicians who performed the autopsy. But only a couple of papers picked up on a small piece of testimony that seemed to have little relevance to the case.

Cleveland had built a case to show that Sarah Mumford's dead body had been placed on the tracks and that members of the Tripp family had been responsible. The medical testimony proved the former. But the case connecting the Tripps to her death still hinged on circumstantial evidence. To place a body on the track to be mutilated by a train was an unthinkable and gruesome way to hide a crime. Cleveland wanted to erase any doubt the jury might have that Lauren, or any other Tripp, could commit such an act. On the last day of the inquest, the coroner had called Lauren Tripp back to the stand.

After the younger Tripp was sworn in, Cleveland hit him with a question that must have taken both Lauren and the jury by surprise. He asked Lauren to give his account of the mysterious death of a child back in November of 1897.

Lauren must have wondered who had leaked this tip to the coroner. He reluctantly explained that the child was a two-month-old baby girl whom he and his wife had named Susan. She had been found dead, Lauren reported, accidentally smothered.

Cleveland's examination of the witness brought out the fact that it had taken the family eight hours to call in a physician. But this was not the fact that Cleveland found most concerning. The point he wanted the jury to hear was that a death certificate had been issued without notification to the coroner as required by law.

New York state had begun regulating the reporting of deaths with an 1880 law requiring that any birth or death be registered with the town clerk. An 1888 addendum posed penalties to those who failed to do so. In the case in question, a child found to be dead with no attending physician, it was required that the county coroner be notified to initiate an inquest into the death.

The blatant defiance of his jurisdiction would have incensed Cleveland. He used the incident to show a pattern of skirting the law to avoid scrutiny.

Just how Cleveland learned of the incident was unclear. The death was not even registered at the Pendleton clerk's office as it should have been. Instead, it was registered in the town of Clarence across the county line. The certificate listed Susan Margret Tripp, aged two months, as dying on November 24, 1897, at 3:00 a.m. Her parents were identified as Lauren and Carrie Tripp. The town of Clarence was recorded as the place of death, a fact that was refuted by Lauren's testimony. The inaccuracy was not the only peculiarity of the record. No physician was listed on the certificate, it was signed only by the Erie County justice of the peace, listed as the acting coroner. Suffocation was recorded as the chief cause of death.

The record also noted that the child was buried in the Shawnee cemetery on Mapleton Road. No marker had been placed.

Depending on Cleveland's informant, Cleveland might not have known about the death record in Erie County. It might have offered further proof of the measures taken by the Tripps to hide the unfortunate death. But what Cleveland most likely had not discovered, because he was only concerned with matters of death, was that the child's birth was also hidden in the Clarence register.

41
Amelia

Amelia wrestled all night with strange dreams. She could see Maud in someone else's arms but could not reach her. When she tried to draw closer, something or someone grabbed her from behind. She fought to escape the grip but the more she struggled the more the hands inflicted pain. Still, she fought harder to get to Maud, who started to cry.

That was when she woke up. Maud cried from her cradle. Amelia moved quickly to quiet her before her parents awoke. She picked Maud up and carried the infant back to her bed. Amelia could still feel her heart pounding from the dream. As she pulled the baby to her breast and closed her eyes, she tried to remember what happened in the nightmare. The details were already fading. But the emotion still held its grip—fear and rage. She suddenly understood something about herself. If someone threatened to take her child, she would fight to her death.

42
Sarah's Story
August 18, 1899

The Statue of Justice crowned the entrance tower of the Niagara County Courthouse. Friday morning, all four members of the Tripp family passed beneath her stare as they entered the twin doors of the limestone structure.

Henry, Matilda, Lauren, and Iva Tripp sat in the courtroom to await the preliminary hearing for their case. They were accompanied by their attorney, Luther Reeves. Reeves, at twenty-seven, was only two years older than Lauren. It was Daniel Brong who served as the more experienced attorney on the Tripp defense team. Mr. Brong, Niagara County's former District Attorney, was well on his way to earning a reputation as a formable criminal legal mind. He was also a Republican party leader who had a gift for rousing orations. But Brong had yet to arrive.

Cleveland took the bench, still in the role of acting magistrate. This posed a peculiar situation since it was the magistrate's duty in a preliminary hearing to decide the merit of the prosecutor's evidence. District Attorney Hopkins presented the case that Cleveland had built and was still actively investigating, a circumstance that might have been contested by the defense attorneys.

But holding a preliminary hearing, versus taking the case directly to a grand jury, created an advantage for the defense.

Grand jury proceedings were held behind closed doors and excluded the accused and their defense team. However biased Cleveland's hearing might have been, it gave the defense a preview of what to expect should they go to trial. It also permitted the accused to see and confront any witness offered by the prosecution.

District Attorney Hopkins recognized a problem with the case. Henry and Lauren Tripp had contradicted each other about the night of Sarah's death. But testimony given by a defendant to a coroner's jury could not be used against them in a trial. Hopkins had a parade of other witnesses to choose from. But he needed witnesses who offered evidence that was neither hearsay nor circumstantial and who would be willing to testify at trial. To make his case, he had to show a crime had occurred and connect the Tripps to that crime. And there was still the unanswered question of motive. What he needed was an eyewitness to the murder or someone with evidence of why Sarah was murdered that night. Cleveland needed to bring him more evidence than that presented at the inquest.

Attorney Brong finally entered the courtroom. As the proceedings began, the Tripp family showed little outward sign of worry.

District Attorney Hopkins stood up and called his first witness.

Dr. Pettit took the stand and swore in. He testified to his examination of the body and his assistance in the autopsy. Pettit related the results just as he had done during the inquest. He described the potentially fatal wounds including a skull fracture and a wound at the base of the brain. Sarah's pelvis had also been crushed. He noted the lack of blood that should have been present. He declared that the girl was dead before the train struck her and that someone placed her lifeless body on the track. Questions by the defense team highlighted the fact that Pettit was unable to definitively say if either wound was the cause of death or caused by the train postmortem.

Dr. Loomis, who had been the lead medical examiner for the autopsy, was out of town on vacation. But Pettit's testimony was solid. Even though he could not give a definitive cause of death, he made it clear that Sarah had not been killed by the train. It offered sufficient evidence that a crime had been committed. The testimony did not, however, answer the question of why Sarah was murdered, or more precisely, why was she killed on June 8th.

Cleveland had arranged for one more witness for the prosecution to present. Unfortunately, illness had prevented their appearance. He was so confident in the importance of this witness to the case that Cleveland called for an adjournment until August 31st.

43
Amelia

"She is beautiful." Mary Shaffer peered down at the sleeping child.

Amelia smiled. "She is, isn't she," she said. "I wish I could show her off, but my mother says it's not proper to be flaunting her around like she has a father."

Mary looked at Amelia like she wanted to tell her something but forgot the words.

"What is it?" Amelia asked.

Mary sat on the edge of Amelia's bed. "I'm expecting. I'll have a baby too," she said, "around Christmastime."

"That's wonderful. Our children will grow to be friends." Amelia wondered if that was true. Their circumstances were so different.

Amelia's mother came into the room and interrupted the girls. "If the baby is sleeping, come into the kitchen to visit," she said. Ricca turned to Mary Shafer. "How's your mother?"

"Her eyes are getting worse, but she makes well of it," Mary responded. "That reminds me," she reached into her dress pocket and pulled something out. "Ma made this for the baby," She handed Amelia a blue crocheted bonnet.

"It's so beautiful," Amelia said. She held the tiny hat in her hand. Aside from the cradle, it was the only gift Maud received. It was not customary to give gifts to a child born to a fallen woman. Amelia's eyes misted at Mrs. Graff's gesture of kindness.

"Tell your mother she shouldn't have fussed, but we thank her for the trouble," Ricca said and returned to the kitchen.

"Yes, please thank her for me." Amelia sat on the bed next to Mary. "We can stay in here to talk if we whisper."

"We can talk about the trial," Mary offered. "It's all over the papers." She reached into her pocket again and pulled out folded-up newspaper clippings. "Here, I cut them from the paper so you could read them for yourself."

"Thank you," Amelia wanted to read them right then but set them aside for later. "Tell me what's happening."

"Well, nothing really, it keeps getting postponed," Mary said. "But there was plenty said at the inquiry. The paper said nearly fifty people spoke, mostly against the Tripp family."

"What did they all say?" Amelia delighted in having answers to the questions that had been swirling in her mind since before Maud came.

"Well, for one thing, some of the neighbors said they saw the Tripp wagon near the tracks that night,"

"I figured they must have had an eyewitness of some kind," Amelia said.

"And they dug up her body so the doctors could examine her properly," Mary said.

Amelia could not imagine such a thing.

"The doctor said she was not in a delicate condition as they thought," Mary said.

"What?" All this time Amelia had felt so connected to Sarah because she believed they had both been in the same condition. She had just assumed the rumors were true. "So why did so many people think she was?"

"Don't know," Mary shrugged. "I read she was large for her age. Maybe people thought she looked that way."

"Could the doctors tell how she died?" Amelia asked.

"They could tell it wasn't the train," Mary said. "George said there wasn't enough blood."

The two girls sat quietly. Amelia had so much new information to sort through. She wished she could talk to the doctors herself. Then she remembered something else.

"Have they written anything about Lauren Tripp's wife?" she asked. "I noticed in the other papers they don't mention her."

"No," Mary responded. "Maybe she was not home when it happened."

"But she was," Amelia replied. "In the interview with the *Times*, Mr. Tripp said his wife went across to their son's house but neither of them had seen her."

"Maybe she was the mystery witness." Mary's eyes widened.

"What mystery witness?"

"There was a witness that did not show up to court. George says that whoever it is, their testimony must be crucial to the case. It's the reason they postponed the hearing." Mary hesitated. "I have something else I need to tell you, but I'm not sure how to say it."

Amelia looked at her friend. Mary held her lips tightly together and gazed toward the floor.

"Just say it," Amelia told her.

"George said Owen left town." She whispered it quickly. "Went out west somewhere."

Amelia felt the words slam against her. A scorching pain tore through her gut, up her throat, and burned against her eyes. But Amelia held back the tears. She did not want Mary to see her cry. She would think she was crying for Owen, but her pain cut much deeper than heartache. For a moment, she felt angry at her friend for bringing her the news, and for having a husband.

Maud let out a cry. Not a full cry but a sleepy utterance of discomfort. Mary looked at the cradle.

"She'll go back to sleep, just leave her," Amelia said.

"Maybe we should go into the kitchen," Mary whispered.

"Maybe we should. You go on out, and I'll get her settled."

As soon as Mary left, Amelia slumped on the bed. She held her eyes tightly shut. She felt alone and wished for someone to talk to. Not Mary Shafer, she was a friend, but she did not know what it was like to carry the burden of shame and to have no prospect for a future.

Amelia slid to the floor. She wished she could break into little pieces and slip between the floorboards. She longed for Annie. Amelia tried to picture her older sister there in the room with her. She imagined Annie's hands on her back.

Maud's cry grew louder. Amelia lifted her head and took a deep breath. She rose to her feet and went to her daughter.

44

Sarah's Story

September 11, 1899

The preliminary hearing on the Tripp case that had been scheduled for August 31st was rescheduled twice and again adjourned until September 16th. Cleveland failed to produce the witness and the testimony that he believed would tie the case together. Dr. Pettit was the only witness who testified.

County officials did not support Cleveland's dogged pursuit of justice for Sarah Mumford or his hunt for the truth. Reports began to circulate that the authorities wished to drop the case due to lack of evidence. District Attorney Hopkins informed the press that he would not hold the case over. He intended to present the case to the grand jury, whether Coroner Cleveland had finished his investigation or not.

The Niagara County Grand Jury convened on a Monday evening. The calendar was one of the largest for a term ever scheduled by the county. The grand jury would be called to deliberate close to a hundred cases during the two-week session. To complete their task, they would need to dispose of six to eight a day. The district attorney and his assistant hustled to prepare for so many cases. Many of the charges involved testimony. In each, the jury was charged with deciding if the case had enough evidence to issue an indictment and go to trial, or if they decided the evidence fell short, they would issue a verdict of 'No Bill.'

The Tripp case was one of the most notorious on the schedule, but not the only homicide. The grand jury was also set to hear the case against Edward Plunkett. Plunkett was charged with murder after the dead body of his travel mate was found in a boxcar in North Tonawanda. The evidence against him seemed strong but mostly circumstantial. Unlike the Tripps, Plunkett could not afford counsel. If the jury handed him an indictment, the county would be required to appoint a defense.

The honorable Judge Henry A. Childs presided over the session held in Lockport at the county courthouse. Childs had been appointed to the bench in 1883. The seasoned judge had a reputation for fairness. He also had a passion for protecting individual rights.

The grand jury's closed proceedings left the Tripp family and all of Pendleton with nothing to do but wait.

45
Amelia

On Saturday, Aunt Katherine brought three parsley roots, two jars of pickled cabbage, and one well-cooked plan.

"I have a solution to your problem," Aunt Katherine said just as soon as she handed Ricca the produce. Before Amelia's mother responded, Katherine continued in German.

"A gentleman in the neighborhood, a businessman, is a responsible provider for his family. His younger brother, maybe not as much. Their family thinks that with a wife, he starts to be more responsible."

"Why are you telling me this, Katherine?" Ricca asked, placing the parsley in a bowl.

"I tell him, my niece needs a husband, your brother needs a wife. Everybody is happy, ja?"

Ricca turned toward Katherine.

"What kind of family are they?" she asked.

"A good family, German, Ja" Aunt Katherine answered. "And they are Christian."

Amelia listened. It seemed ironic that Aunt Katherine pushed marriage when hers had held so much sorrow. She heard her parents whisper about it many times in German. Once, in a drunken rage, Uncle Fritz struck their 16-year-old daughter and locked her out of the house on a cold night. Lucy fell ill and died two months later. Katherine blamed her husband. But she endured several more years of drunken violence before she finally took the rest of the children and moved to North Tonawanda.

"What kind of businessman?" Ricca asked.

"An innkeeper," Aunt Katherine said.

"A saloon, you mean."

"Ja, Ja, a saloon. It is a good business," Aunt Katherine said.

Amelia did not like it anymore that they talked in front of her like she was not there.

"I don't think that sounds like a good place for a baby," Ricca said.

"Be reasonable, Ricca, Amelia is a fallen woman, she has not a lot of options." Katherine held up her hands for emphasis.

"I don't know," Ricca said.

Amelia's face flushed. She had been childish before to think her mother had hidden her out of shame. Ricca had meant to protect her, always.

Aunt Katherine turned to Amelia. "Amelia, you trust your Tanta, Ja?"

Amelia studied her aunt's face. She saw tenacity borne of necessity in every well-defined line. Even though she had never actually divorced, Aunt Katherine had raised her children on her own. Amelia had been inspired by her aunt's courage. But her situation was different. Aunt Katheryn had faced disgrace, but she was never a 'fallen woman.' And Amelia knew that her mother could not shield her forever.

46

Sarah's Story

September 28, 1899

The grand jury's deliberation lasted three days longer than expected. The Tripp family remained home on bond for the duration. Edward Plunkett, the young man accused of shooting his travel mate and leaving him to die in a boxcar, waited in the county jail.

On Thursday, the grand jury rose to announce their decisions. They had acted on 102 cases, including the Plunkett case. The jury found enough evidence to hold Edward Plunkett over for trial. He was indicted for murder in the first degree. Plunkett pleaded not guilty.

The Tripps were more fortunate. The grand jury declared 'no bill' as they failed to find enough evidence against Henry, Lauren, Matilda, or Iva.

The decision did not come as a shock. Many had speculated that the case brought before the jury hinged on circumstantial evidence. Even the District Attorney doubted the strength of the case.

Cleveland must have been deflated. He had spent months methodically following all leads and examining every detail. Yet, he failed to bring forth the evidence that tied his theories together.

The coroner might have turned the case over and over in his mind. The first theory proposed by Henry Tripp was that

Sarah had run off and was hit by the train as she headed toward Lockport. Or as first suggested by the railway agent, she committed suicide. The evidence eliminated both possibilities. The next theory was that she had been abducted outside the Tripp property. If he believed Henry Tripp's timeline, this would have happened between 9:00 and 10:00 p.m. The already dead body had been placed on the track almost three miles away sometime before midnight. The search party had begun by 10:00. No one claimed to see anyone other than the Tripp wagon on the roads. Cleveland dismissed the possibility that Sarah had been abducted.

Most people believed that Sarah's lifeless body was placed on the tracks by a member of the Tripp family, but that her death was unintended. The *Buffalo Evening News* reported that an official on the case whose name could not be mentioned believed this to be the instance. But without motive, they could not prove murder.

Whether by murder or by accident, the evidence seemed to point to Sarah's death having occurred on one of the Tripp properties. But even Cleveland would have to admit that there were still unanswered questions. If it had been an accident, what provoked the incident on that night, and what compelled the Tripp family to go to such great lengths to cover it up?

Perhaps the unnamed witness who failed to testify because of illness might have provided the answers.

In the end, critics panned Coroner Cleveland for moving too slowly and allowing the investigation to drag on too long. The biggest criticism he received was for not searching Tripp's property. If the Tripps had a hand in Sarah's death, then the Tripp homestead would have been a potential crime scene. The problem, critics failed to acknowledge, was that Cleveland had not initially known a crime had been committed. Far too much time had passed before he discovered evidence that Sarah had been murdered and that the Tripp property could possibly be the scene of the crime.

But there were those in Pendleton who had their suspicions right from the start and those who always would.

The following Monday Henry, Matilda, Lauren, and Iva Tripp rode to Lockport to appear for the last time before Coroner Cleveland. Cleveland released them each from their bail bond. The Tripps departed the Courthouse, through the twin doors, down the steps, and past the gaze of lady justice, free from further scrutiny of the law.

47
Amelia

"I don't know why people would expect anything different," Ricca said to her husband. Amelia listened to her parents discuss the grand jury verdict. She had lost the desire to talk about it. It seemed so unjust and just one more tragedy that she would never be able to understand.

Someone knocked on the front door. Amelia's father looked at his wife. Ricca shrugged and went to the front room to answer the door.

"I hope I'm not interrupting," Dr. Helwig said, "but I was coming past from Lockport and thought I'd check to see how the young girl and her baby were doing?"

Ricca stepped aside and gestured for the doctor to come in.

"I'll go get Maud," Amelia jumped up to retrieve the sleeping baby from her room.

When she returned Doctor Helwig was seated in the seldom-used front room. She handed Maud over to him.

"Well, she looks like she is growing just fine," he said. Amelia smiled nervously. She wanted the doctor to see she was taking good care of her. Dr. Helwig pulled a speculum from his bag and began examining the baby. "How've you been feeling?" he asked Amelia.

"Much more like normal," she said.

"Any concerns?" Dr. Helwig asked.

"Can I ask you something?" said Amelia.

"Yes, of course." He handed Maud back to her mother.

Amelia reached for the baby and settled Maud in her arms. "Can you really tell by the blood if a body was dead before the train hit it?"

The doctor looked puzzled. Amelia guessed this was not the question he had expected. He folded his stethoscope back in his black bag. Realization passed over his face.

"I was not the medical examiner on the case," he said, "but yes, it's possible."

"Then somebody got away with murder," Amelia said.

Helwig sighed heavily. "You have to trust the justice system."

"But there was no justice," Amelia said. "Not for Sarah."

Helwig sat in silence. He had no response.

"I think she knew too much of the truth about someone," Amelia said. "People don't always like the truth." She thought about Owen and remembered what the doctor had done for her. Amelia turned her attention to the baby, who started to get fussy.

"Perhaps," Dr. Helwig said. "But the court required evidence that just wasn't there."

"Seems to me like they just gave up on her," Amelia said quietly. She still had so many unanswered questions. Sarah tried to get help from the neighbors. But no one helped her then and no one was helping her now. "Why can't they be held responsible for the way they treated her?" As soon as Amelia spoke the words, she knew the answer. Whatever crimes had been committed on the Tripp farm; they were crimes from which people had become comfortable turning their heads. What disturbed Amelia about Sarah's story was not just what the Tripps had hidden, but what they did not have to.

48
Sarah's Story
October 26, 1899

The theater train pulled away from Lockport station on its Buffalo excursion brimming with well-attired passengers. The crowd appeared dressed for a prestigious affair. Their clothing marked the occasion, and the fashionable Lockport society held nothing back tonight.

This was no ordinary Thursday. The passengers brimmed with anticipation of the night's performance. Buffalo's own Star Theater hosted the Official World Premier of William Gillette and Sir Arthur Conan Doyle's *Sherlock Holmes*. The four-act drama brought to life, for the first time, the immensely popular detective. Their thirst for mystery, left unquenched by the summer's events, would finally be satisfied.

They rolled past Mapleton station with little regard to the quiet cemetery not a quarter of a mile outside their windows. A twice-dug grave sat in the center of the graveyard. The dirt-covered mound collected newly fallen leaves. A white stone waited for the ground to settle to be placed. On it was inscribed only two words, Sarah Mumford.

The stone marked no date. Her birthdate was unknown to anyone in Pendleton. Her death date was incorrectly recorded in the official death record as June 9th, the morning her body was struck by the train.

Buried aside her grave without a marker was the infant daughter of Lauren Tripp.

As they continued through Pendleton, Sherlock Holmes still captured the focus of the theater train riders. The true crime that had unfolded on the very same tracks less than five months prior had lost their attention.

Since the grand jury found no bill against the Tripps, the investigation was closed. The newspapers carried not a single story regarding Sarah Mumford or who was responsible for her tragic death. The mystery remained unsolved for more than one hundred and twenty years. But a stone marker placed next to her grave more than a year later would reveal an important clue.

1900

49
Sarah's Story
March 6, 1900

Sarah Mumford's death was not the first case Cleveland and Dr. Pettit investigated together. But it was their last. The long inquest and preliminary hearing took a toll on all involved.

Dr. Pettit gave up practicing medicine shortly after the grand jury's verdict. Not yet fifty, he cited failing health as the reason. Instead, the innovative physician founded a business, Pettit and Company, manufacturing mattresses. The career change proved successful. A few years later he received a patent for a machine he invented to make tufts.

Less than four months after the grand jury had found "No Bill" against the Tripps, an exhausted Henry Cleveland contracted typhoid pneumonia. In February, his condition became so severe that friends took turns sitting by the coroner's bedside. His medical care was under the direction of Dr. Loomis.

But by March, he had made a remarkable turn for the better. Dr. Loomis declared he had fully recovered and that he could resume his official role as the county coroner by the end of the month. On March 6, Cleveland would have been still home healing. Perhaps he passed his time while recovering by reading through local papers. If so, he might have noticed a small item on page 8 of the *Niagara Sun* that read:

"Clarence D., infant son of Mr. and Mrs. Lauren Tripp, died at their home at Mapleton, March 2, 1900, aged 11 months."

This item might have puzzled Cleveland. No mention of another infant child of Lauren had been reported at the time of the inquest. If Cleveland calculated, he would have noted the child's birth to have been in early April of 1899, a few weeks before Sarah Mumford's visit to the Millers and two months before her death.

This would have raised many questions for the coroner.

A check in the Pendleton town birth registry would have confirmed a baby boy was born in Mapleton on April 5, 1899. The record listed Lauren and Carrie Tripp as the parents. But the physician recorded the child's name as Raymond, not Clarence.

Cleveland might have thought about witnesses so certain that Sarah had been pregnant.

Cleveland no doubt still regretted the assumption that Sarah had been killed by the train when her lifeless body was discovered on the tracks. It cost them an opportunity to gather precious evidence. But what other assumptions had he made? When Mapleton residents insisted that Sarah had been pregnant, did he assume, like everyone else, it meant she had been pregnant when she died? When the autopsy proved otherwise, did he wrongly assume that the story had no merit?

Was this the child neighbors had believed Sarah was carrying in her womb? George Miller testified that Sarah had been hidden for eleven months before her death. *Was this to conceal a pregnancy?*

It was not uncommon for a married family member to claim an illegitimate child as their own. *But if Sarah had been pregnant, who impregnated the then 14-year-old girl? Was it intentional? And was this the first time?* This might have reminded Cleveland of the incident of the child born in 1897 whose birth and death were improperly registered in Erie County.

The Pendleton death registry recorded the death of Raymond Tripp in Mapleton on March 2, 1900. The record revealed the child to be ten months and 27 days old. Raymond and Clarence were the same child. The cause of death was listed as Measles/meningitis. Pendleton experienced a small outbreak of measles earlier that year but with no fatalities. Unfortunately, eleven-month-old Raymond lacked the immunity to fight the virus. Something that might be indicative of a child that had not been breastfed by his mother.

A month later, Carrie went back to Michigan by herself for a three-week visit with her family. In the Shawnee cemetery, someone placed a small stone next to Sarah Mumford's tombstone to mark the grave of an infant. The engraving read 'Infant son of Lauren Tripp': no name, no date, no mother.

Sometime after March of 1900, a second larger stone was purchased to memorialize both children, the one lost in 1900 and the one lost in 1897. The new gravestone was placed in front of the smaller stone and less than two feet from Sarah's headstone. It contained two names, no dates. A simple inscription read:

Susan M. & Clarence D.
children of L.S. and C.E. Tripp

Coroner Cleveland was not able to follow up on any of this. On April 11, his fever returned, and he died three days later. The news shocked friends and colleagues who claimed the 44-year-old had never looked healthier. No inquest was held.

1901

50
January 9, 1901

An ominous silence crept through the Rochester Orphan Asylum. Miss Ashdown, the night nurse, completed her 10:00 p.m. rounds. Children filled the long white rows of beds in each of the dormitories, tucked in for the night. In the third-floor infirmary, an attendant watched over two children sick with diphtheria. Miss Brad had only recently recovered from the same infliction. The matron, Miss Dinehart, had retired for the night.

The first-floor laundry encompassed the southwest corner of the building. In contrast to the daytime bustle of wash work, it sat uninhabited and silent except for the soft hiss of an open gas jet.

At 1:00 a.m., Miss Ashdown smelled smoke and ran to the window. She saw flames billowing from the west wing. Her first instinct was to arouse the children. She then awoke the matron. Miss Dinehart phoned the police headquarters and instructed Nurse Ashdown to ring the janitor who slept in a separate building on the property.

Smoke rose to the dorms directly above the laundry and rendered the sleeping children unconscious. Small explosions reverbed in the ears of those in other parts of the Asylum.

Firemen raced to the scene to douse the blaze. Sleepy children poured out of the building to safety. But women and children were still trapped on the upper floors.

Miss Brad heard the commotion and knew she had to get the sick children to safety. She gathered them as best as she could and headed toward the stairs. To her horror, flames engulfed the only way out. In desperation, she retreated to the roof with the children.

The fire searched for something to consume. It devoured the wooden staircase climbing to the third floor at a greater speed than it spread sideways.

When Miss Brad realized the firemen could not reach them on the roof, she carried the children back down to the smoke-filled infirmary to a window. Firemen helped the weakened attendant and the lifeless children down a ladder and away from the fire.

Firemen worked to save as many children as possible. They employed ladders to reach the trapped children. The flames blocked the only two fire escapes. In desperation, an attendant named Martha Gillis jumped to her death.

Twenty-six children and two adults perished that night. Over the next two days, three more died in the hospital, including Miss Brad, who might have been able to save herself but refused to leave the children in her care. The total loss of lives was thirty-one.

The tragedy left the city of Rochester stunned. In the days that followed, numerous citizens flocked to the scene to view the unthinkable destruction. Flags flew half-mast in mourning. Hospitals and private homes volunteered beds for the tiny survivors left without shelter. All around the city, fire drills rang through schools. Superintendents recommitted to diligent preparation for everyone's worst fears.

The coroner of Monroe County, Henry Kleindienst, initiated an investigation and ruled the deaths accidental. His report highlighted the measures that might have prevented such a loss of life. Had a night watchman been hired, he could have assisted in the rescue. The large institute had only two fire escapes. The fire marshal had not conducted an inspection in over two years. The coroner directed blame on the Board of Trustees.

"Trustees were such in name only and did nothing but look after the funds of the institute and partake of the social functions."

As tragedies often do, this one triggered introspection and a call for change. The fire marshal advocated for the purchase of nets to save future lives. Officials called for stricter rules about inspections and fire escapes in large buildings used to house vulnerable inmates.

The fire illuminated the ills of the orphan asylum, not just in Rochester, but across the state. The call for reform, once a murmur, became a roar. The board of the Rochester Orphan Asylum vowed never again to place dormitories above the ground floor. When it came time to rebuild, they adopted the cottage model. This progressive approach created smaller home-like environments for children in need of care. From the ashes rose the model for a new era of reform.

Despite being denied a license by the New Your State Board of Charities, William Jarvis Maybee continued to place children. In 1901, the Society for the Prevention of Cruelty to Children launched an investigation into his practices. The *Utica Observer* reported on the case that sparked the investigation.

"As a result of this system, a case of cruelty toward a 12-year-old girl has been unearthed in the northern part of Oneida County. The child was taken from its parents by the Reverend

Jarvis W. Maybee and given a home with a family, where it remained for about a year when she was again given to another family, who ill-treated the girl, compelling her to clean spittoons and do other work in a barroom. It is claimed she was cruelly whipped and beaten and otherwise ill-treated. A few months ago, the child disappeared, having been removed, it is supposed, by friends who had learned of her surroundings and who desired to befriend her. When found she begged not to be returned, and a home was temporarily found for her."

The Oneida County court indicted Maybee and charged him with placing destitute children without authority. But the judge dismissed the charges due to insufficient evidence that any child had been harmed by Maybee's unorthodox practices. Maybee, it seemed, still had powerful supporters.

Maybee's story did not end there. He left New York and headed south. He settled in Virginia where he continued his work without disclosing his experience in New York State.

51
Amelia
June 19, 1901

Amelia lifted herself onto her elbows so she could watch her mother. It went quicker this time. But her labor came with greater pain. Ricca gently cleaned up the crying baby and brought her back to Amelia. She did not bother to swaddle the child, just laid her on her mother's chest. Amelia leaned back; her hair matted to her face and over her soft blue eyes. She was too tired to look at her baby girl. She just placed her hands on her tiny back and held her close to her pounding heart.

The doctor removed a notebook from his black leather bag. "Is this your first child?" he asked. It was not Dr. Helwig.

"No," Amelia answered. "It's my second."

"First one still alive?" the doctor asked, without looking up.

"Yes," responded Amelia. The doctor jotted it down in the notebook.

"And the name?

"I want to name her Mary," Amelia said. He wrote it down.

"And the name of the mother?" he asked, as if it might be someone other than the girl lying in the bed holding the infant.

"Amelia Knople," she answered, "and the father's name is William G - L - A -"

The doctor interrupted her. "Where is the father?" he asked.

“He couldn’t be here,” Amelia said, “but he knows about the baby. We are set to be married.”

The doctor shook his head. ‘I cannot list the name if you are not married.”

“But we will be,” Amelia protested.

“Why didn’t you marry after your first child?” the doctor asked.

Amelia’s cheeks warmed. “It’s not the same father,” she said softly.

The doctor slowly shook his head and crumpled his mouth. “‘Out of wedlock’ is all I can put.” He closed the book and slipped it back into his bag.

Amelia felt the shame conveyed by the words ‘out of wedlock’ but harbored no anger for the doctor. It was she alone who carried that burden. But she worried it would fall on the shoulders of her small child.

The doctor left the room without a word to either woman. Ricca stared hard until he shut the door behind him. “Once you’re married,” Amelia’s mother said, as if she heard her thoughts, “No one will remember that the baby came first.”

Amelia heard a tiny bit of desperation at her mother’s assurance. She knew her parents’ support was unwavering, but she also knew the burden another child would bring to the already stretched household. Her father was sixty, and he labored every day to eke out a living for the four of them and keep up on the mortgage.

Ricca gathered the soaked sheets and rags from the foot of the bed. Amelia felt the tininess of the infant in her arms. William had agreed to marry her and be a father to Maud and the baby. They planned to live with his father in North Tonawanda until William earned enough for their own place.

Amelia did not believe she had a choice in the matter. Just like she did not believe she had a choice to refuse William's advances. She had already been soiled.

Amelia closed her eyes and tried to picture something nice. The Pan-American Exhibition had begun the previous month in Buffalo. Trolleys carried North Tonawanda residents to and from the World's Fair. Amelia wanted to bring Maud before it ended in November. She had heard and read all about the event that had been planned for more than two years. She even saw a sketch of the fairgrounds on a flyer that William had shown her. But nothing matched what she envisioned in her mind. Fountain-lined walkways led to exhibits filled with modern inventions and exotic creatures from far-off places, air filled with the aroma of fried potatoes, all washed down with a sip of sarsaparilla. Amelia read that an entire hall had been dedicated to the accomplishments of women. And of course, there were the lights. People came from all over the world to see the fairgrounds illuminated by electric lights each evening. It made Amelia smile to think of her daughters growing up in a world where darkness could be banished with the throw of a switch.

The baby whimpered. Amelia looked down at her newborn child so weak and helpless. When she was a child, Amelia's parents made the decisions. She had once looked forward to adulthood and deciding her own course in life. But it seemed to Amelia that her world had been growing dimmer and her choices narrowed. Her decisions belonged to her children now, whatever choices she had left in life she would make for them.

1902

52
Sarah's Story
March 27, 1902

The Grand Jury's findings dismissed the Tripp family from further scrutiny of the law but not from the scrutiny of their neighbors. Lauren had gained the attention he craved. But life in the small village could not have been comfortable.

The family did not remain in Pendleton. When Lauren and Carrie left, the Mapleton section of the *Lockport Journal* reported the event with one curt sentence. "Lauren Tripp has just moved his family and belongings from here; has found work north of Lockport." Henry Tripp had sold his farm earlier that year. He and Matilda settled in the town of Cambria just north of Pendleton.

Lauren never amounted to all he bragged to be. He struggled to keep employed and maintain a proper household. Henry tried to support him. He cosigned a tenant agreement for his son, but when Lauren failed to pay the rent for eight months straight, both he and his father were taken to court. Lauren's excuse was that the house was run-down and not worth the rent. Once again, Henry Tripp stood by his son, but the judge found in favor of his landlord.

Lauren and Carrie moved to Batavia, New York, for a few years, and then to Toledo, Ohio, less than thirty miles from Carrie's hometown in Michigan. They never had children.

Eventually, Carrie Tripp divorced Lauren. She cited extreme and repeated cruelty as her reason. Carrie returned to her home in Michigan and moved in with an unmarried sister. When she died, her obituary ran in the *Adrian Daily Telegram.*

Mrs. Carrie Tripp

> Mrs. Carrie E. Tripp, 75 years old, died this morning at 2 o'clock in the home of her sister Mrs. Lillian Dersham of 334 South McKenzie Street with whom she had lived for the last ten years. She had been ill only a few days.
>
> Mrs. Tripp was born in Palmyra. Sept. 5, 1870, and spent her entire life in Palmyra and Adrian. She is survived by her sister and several nieces and nephews.
>
> The funeral will be Wednesday at 2 p.m. in the Braun Funeral Home, the Rev. John E. Martin officiating. The burial will be in Pleasant View Cemetery at Blissfield.

The newspaper made no mention of her marriage, the time she spent in New York, or the babies buried hundreds of miles away.

Lauren moved back to Niagara County to live the remainder of his life. He was buried next to his sister Iva in the Shawnee Cemetery, twenty feet from the grave of Sarah Mumford.

1903

53
Amelia

Amelia stood at the doorway of the small shack. Aunt Katherine beckoned the front stoop with a handful of herbs. "I brought them for a tea, to ease your pains. We can go inside, and I will brew a pot, Ja."

"It's a mess," Amelia explained, "and I just got the baby to sleep."

"But it is not proper for a woman in your condition to stand on the street."

Amelia sighed and placed her hand on her large belly. "It feels good out here," she said. "It has been so hot for September." It was the last day of summer, but it felt like the middle of July.

"Ja." Aunt Katherine did not push.

"How did you find me?" Amelia asked. She had not told her family that Williams' father had thrown them out. She meant to wait until they found a more presentable home.

"I ask and people tell me." Aunt Katherine responded. "I promised your mama I would give you a message."

Amelia felt a pull in her heart at the mention of her mother. She longed for her, yet it grew harder and harder to face her.

"Your papa is sick again, and she cannot leave him now," Aunt Katherine said. "But as soon as she can, she will come to help with the new baby."

"Is it serious?"

"Ja, your father is old and tired, and I sense his heart is growing weaker." Aunt Katherine gently closed her eyes. When Uncle Fritz died of kidney failure the previous year, Amelia's father signed an affidavit on Katherine's behalf, so she would receive his widow's pension. Whatever rift she had with her brother-in-law had softened.

"Tell Mama not to worry, William's sisters check on me," she said, "and the neighbors are kind." Amelia glanced around at her surroundings. North Tonawanda felt so different from Pendleton. In town, the houses butted closer together, but neighbors seemed more detached.

"And your husband brings you what you need for the children?" Aunt Katherine asked.

Amelia did not want to tell Aunt Katherine that she had not seen her husband in days. Marriage had not made life easier for Amelia. She had three children under the age of four and one more by the end of the month. William liked to drink, and he took his rage out on her. Amelia forgot that Aunt Katherine knew what it was like to endure a violent husband.

"Minnie took Maud and Mary, just until I have the baby," Amelia said. "I'm still nursing the boy." William's brother Charles and his wife Minnie had a daughter the same age as Maud. Maud played so well with Ruth, that it made sense for her and Mary to stay with them. North Tonawanda had a kindergarten for children not old enough for first grade. Minnie had enrolled her daughter. Amelia remembered how much she enjoyed learning, and Ricca taught her to value education. She wanted that for Maud. If she stayed with the family above the saloon, Maud could walk to school with Ruth.

"You send for me if you need help, Ja." Aunt Katherine said.

"I'll be fine," Amelia said.

Aunt Katherine handed her the herbs and nodded her head.

"Danka."

Aunt Katherine turned and walked toward the ally. She leaned on a stick to steady her crooked body. Amelia guessed it would take her close to an hour to walk the mile back to her home. She felt the urge to call out to her aunt and tell her the truth about her circumstances. But she let it pass. What could the old women do other than put some curse on William.

It was not easy for Amelia to ask for help. She had learned to survive from one day to the next. She had tried to get the authorities to intervene. But with each failed attempt, the situation worsened. So, she resolved that she had to rely on herself to find a way through.

She wiped the sweat from her brow. She knew Aunt Katherine was right about standing outside in her condition. But at least on the stoop, she could feel a breeze. The temperature had not dipped below eighty in three days, and the shack felt like an oven.

She stepped back inside and left the door open a crack. Her efforts to make the small structure look like a home had failed. The gaps in the floorboards let in more sun than the window. Amelia was afraid to scrub too hard on the broken glass, so they remained coated in an amber film. She stood for a moment in the back room, Amelia felt the sweat dripping under her dress and down her legs. It felt more like a stream than a drizzle. She looked down to see a puddle forming on the wood floor. It was not sweat.

"I'm not ready," she cried out loud. No one heard.

54

Amelia's Story

October 18, 1903

On Friday, Mrs. Brauer stepped out her back door, careful not to spill the bowl of soup. Her young neighbor was sick, and Mrs. Brauer didn't know if she had anyone else to help her. She crossed the ally to the small rundown shack. As she drew closer, she heard the faint cry of the newborn. Mrs. Bauer knocked softly at the door. She did not wait long for a response. When she checked on her earlier, the poor girl had been so weak that she refused any food. Mrs. Bauer pushed the door open and stepped into the house. A sour stench hit her nose as she walked to the back room. She peered into the bedroom, set down the soup, and turned to get help.

When the authorities arrived, they found Amelia barely hanging on to life. She cradled a frail infant girl in her arms. Next to her, Amelia's year-old son lay dead. Help had not arrived fast enough.

Amelia and her newborn were both rushed to Twin City Hospital. Their conditions were reported as serious. Amelia's pulse weakened, but she made it through the night. So did her infant daughter.

The next day, Amelia showed no improvement. The doctors might have recognized the signs that an infection had entered her bloodstream. But little could be done to stop the inevitable. Her organs had already begun to slowly shut down.

Amelia died Sunday night. The baby died the next morning.

The hospital notified the coroner. Dr. Helwig, the physician who delivered Amelia's first child, now held the county position. The attending physician briefed the new coroner on the condition in which they were found. Dr. Helwig might have recognized the name of the young girl whom he met before. The circumstances of the deaths disturbed Helwig. He opened an inquest and led the investigation, determined to seek justice for Amelia and her children.

He first interviewed Mrs. Brauer, the neighbor who tried to help Amelia.

"On the 16th of October she appeared to be quite sick," Mrs. Brauer said. "I made her bed and the next day I brought her something to eat but she wanted nothing."

Helwig asked about Amelia's husband. Mrs. Brauer told him that she knew nothing about the family's affairs.

Helwig interviewed another neighbor who lived next door to the hovel Amelia and the children had been living in. Mrs. Randall confirmed that the baby, whom Amelia had named Marie, had been born on September 21st. She had been to the house since the child's birth but not since Amelia had become sick.

"I found everything about the house very filthy. She had almost nothing to wear and the children were very poorly clad." Helwig pressed for more information about Amelia's husband. "She made no complaint about her husband. But she said she had to get up and work as there was no one to do for her." Mrs. Randall said.

The *Buffalo Evening News* carried the story with the headline: "Three Deaths in One Family: Tonawanda Mother and Children Said to Have Been Shamefully Neglected." The community responded with concern. People wondered how such a tragedy could happen. The press turned to Helwig for more answers. "I have not reached any conclusions relative to the death of Mrs. Glawf and children, as I have not concluded the investigation which began yesterday," Helwig said. "It was decided not to perform an autopsy, as there was no doubt that the direct cause of Mrs. Glawf's death was septicemia or blood poisoning. As to whether the poisoning was due to neglect, I cannot say at this stage of the investigation." Dr. Helwig knew that postpartum septicemia could develop from infections weeks after delivery. Especially if a new mother did not have proper care. But he still needed to make sense of the senseless. He searched for someone to blame.

Helwig tried to learn more about Amelia's husband's role in her death. William could not be found. So, Helwig interviewed Amelia's sisters-in-law, Mrs. Witt and Mrs. Hallis. Amelia "seemed to get along all right until five days before her death. She then began to fail." Mary Witt said. "We both brought her food and milk when she was sick." Unfortunately, no one called for medical help until Mrs. Brauer found her on Friday. Then the city took charge of their care, but it was too late for Amelia and her children.

Dr. Helwig recognized the consistency of what he heard and septicemia. Amelia had not received hygienic care or the opportunity for rest and recovery. Perhaps, he had been driven to hold someone accountable for the tragic deaths. But though preventable, septicemia after childbirth still took too many lives to attribute the death to anything other than natural causes. Helwig was bound by the norms of the time. So was Amelia.

At the turn of the century, there were no domestic violence shelters to turn to. But Amelia stood up for herself. At least twice she filed assault charges. This resulted in William being fined $5, then $15, making him angry and providing him with a reason to blame Amelia for his failure to provide for his children. Amelia even tried filing a charge for non-support. But she did not follow through. If he went to jail, there would be no way to feed the children.

Amelia's official cause of death was septicemia. Dr. Helwig determined that her newborn died of malnutrition. Her year-old son died of convulsions, possibly the result of severe dehydration.

On the Wednesday following their deaths, a funeral for Amelia and her baby girl was held at Wattengel's Undertaking room in North Tonawanda. The Charitable Society for the Poor paid for a burial in an unmarked grave in the pauper's section of the same city cemetery where her sister Rachael was buried. Her husband's family likely took care of the arrangements for her year-old son.

Amelia's husband William, faced with assault charges, fled town. By the following spring, he had found work as a farmhand outside of Oneida. While operating a hay bailer, a rope snapped, and the heavy sweep thrust back and rammed William in the gut. The other workers saw the force of the blow and rushed him to the city hospital. There he lay in agony for five days, wracked with fever and surrounded by strangers. On June 4, 1904, the doctor sent Charles a telegram informing him of his brother's condition. A half-hour later, Charles received a second telegram that William had died. The attending physician recorded the death as acute peritonitis. Like Amelia, they buried him in an unmarked grave.

The newspaper chronicled the story of the deaths and investigation. The articles either referred to Amelia as Mrs.

William Glawf or simply 'the mother'. There was no mention of her first name, her family, or the whereabouts of her daughters Maud and Mary.

On October 18th, the day Amelia died, Ricca sat at her husband's deathbed. Amelia's father suffered from cardiomyopathy and pneumonia. He died on November 11, 1903. The word of Amelia and the children's death had reached Ricca by then.

Maud became an orphan in the eyes of the state. Two-year-old Mary had a father, and his family claimed her like they had William's son. When her father skipped town, the neighbor of his brother took her in and raised her as their own. But Maud's father, Owen, had never returned to Niagara County, and his family likely knew nothing of his daughter.

Maud sat in Miss Holmes' classroom at Pine Woods Elementary the day the authorities came and took her to an orphanage. She would never see her sister Mary again. Niagara County orphans were deposited at the Home for the Friendless. The orphanage sat on a spacious campus on the outskirts of Lockport. The institute held 58 children all under the age of thirteen.

The enormity of Ricca's grief would have been overwhelming. She had lost all seven of her children and her husband. She would have been desperate for the grandchild, whom she helped raise for the first two years of her life, to return to her.

Ricca evaluated her situation. She had a home. But at her age, Ricca could not work the farm and care for a young child by herself. Maud needed a home, but without an income, a home was not enough. Orphanages at the time were still less likely to return a child to a destitute family than they were to send them to a workhouse. But the Lockport Orphanage had recognized the need to find safe homes for children placed in their care. They had recently hired a home visitor devoted solely to finding suitable homes in which to place the orphans. Mr. Bayliss rode on horseback across Niagara and neighboring Orleans County to visit prospective households and check up on the children placed out in homes.

Ricca did not want her granddaughter to be raised in an orphanage or to be given to strangers. She believed that children belonged with family. She leaned into her grief until it steadied her.

As Maud lingered at the county orphanage, Ricca and her good friend Freda Graff devised a plan. Ricca moved in with the Graff family. Freda–who was ten years younger than Ricca and had a husband and two children not much older than Maud–would provide a more traditional family environment. Ricca could lease the Knople land to a neighboring farmer to produce an income. She could contribute financially to the household and help her friend who had lost her vision.

The arrangement satisfied the authorities. They returned 4-year-old Maud to the Graff home and into the arms of her grandmother.

Ricca must have sensed that she did not have much time. Before her death, she signed the deed to the property on Bear Ridge Road to Freda Graff. Women could not vote, but New York was one of the few states that allowed women to own real estate. The arrangement provided an income for Maud's care and ensured that she inherited the land that had been in the family for four generations.

Freda made sure Maud knew she was a Knople. She shared the names and stories of her Grandparents. But Maud never heard her mother's name or the story of what happened to her. Maud would be disconnected from the tragedy of her past, but Amelia would be forgotten. Her story hid from her grandchildren. Ricca's decisions and actions would forever set the course for her descendants.

Epilogue

Sometimes the greatest form of justice is the truth.

I wrote Amelia's last chapter in a non-fiction narrative. Maud was my grandmother. I had spent more than twenty years researching the hidden identity and story of her mother, Amelia. This was how I first came across the story of Sarah Mumford.

I wrote Sarah's story as narrative nonfiction so that the truth–or as much as we know of it–could finally be told. Sarah deserved that. I also wanted to present the facts as they unfolded over one hundred and twenty years ago so readers could unravel the mystery for themselves.

As I mentioned in the preface, Amelia's perspective was informed by my research of her life as well as documented accounts of what Pendleton residents thought about the murder. I had been careful not to create anything in the dialogue that would change the facts of Sarah's case.

I chose the title–not just because both girls were hidden–but for the many ways the truth was hidden. My quest to uncover the truth took almost as many twists and turns as the investigation into Sarah's death. Many discoveries surprised me. One of the boys accused by Henry Tripp was indeed my great-great grandmother Ricca's stepbrother. This fact I discovered after I had decided to write the stories together. But the most shocking twist was the discovery of the two infants born to the Tripp family and what appeared to be an attempt to conceal their identity.

I also ran into strange hurdles along the way. I searched for the transcripts from the coroner's inquest at the Niagara County Courthouse. Though they were able to locate Amelia's four-page coroner's report, they were unable to find the 300-page report from Sarah's Inquest. Was it lost to time or was it hidden 124 years ago? I pieced together the testimony from dozens of newspaper articles. However, I still do not know who the mystery witness was or who tipped Cleveland off to the baby born in 1897. I hoped that more information might have been reported in the *Tonawanda News* since some of the original rumors seemed to have come from North Tonawanda. However, I found that the entire year of 1899 of the *Tonawanda News* was missing from both the library's and the historical society's microfilm collection. I found many newspaper articles mentioning that Sarah went by the name Mary Ross. I found no documentation explaining why. These pieces of the story remain hidden.

Over the years, there's been much speculation about who killed Sarah Mumford. But perhaps that's not the right question. Rather we should ask "Who placed Sarah's body on the tracks, and what did they hope to hide?" The answer might not be murder, but I believe the crimes committed were no less sinister. Sarah had likely been part of a system that misused and exploited vulnerable children to benefit others. Today we might call it human trafficking. In 1899, it was barely recognized as a crime. How many more stories like Sarah's remain hidden? And what lengths were taken to hide the truth?

It is my opinion, based on my research, that Lauren Tripp placed Sarah's body on the tracks that night. That was one of the popular theories 124 years ago. The question remained, why? Based on the clues I found, I believe that 15-year-old Sarah gave birth to Lauren Tripp's child before she died. Perhaps she tried to see the baby or threatened to tell someone. It is possible a struggle led to her death. I think it was even more plausible that she died the same way as Amelia, without proper care or medical treatment after the birth of a child. The cover-up hid the identity of the infant.

I don't think the mystery will ever be completely solved, but I uncovered more pieces to the puzzle. I hope that other history detectives can continue the search. I included my research notes for that reason.

But this story is about something bigger than "Who killed Sarah Mumford?" It is about the treatment of women and children at the turn of the century and the disregard for the lives of the marginalized. It is about the value of family connection and the importance of choice and voice as we continue to reform our systems. And it is about helping the hidden to be seen. Most importantly, it is about how even lives cut short by tragedy impact the fabric of humanity.

Sarah had no descendants to tell her story. Both Sarah's sisters married but neither had children. Their mother Cora eventually got out of the state hospital and remarried. She lived until 1922. Grace died three years before her mother. Kittie lived until 1947. Sadly, she died at the same State hospital in which her mother resided.

The trouble with writing nonfiction is you can't change what actually happened. I would have preferred an ending that resulted in justice for at least one of the girls. But I began my journey as a quest for the truth. Because when the truth is hidden, it loses its power to heal.

I wish I could write that Maud went on to have an easy life. The truth is, she lived a hard life. She raised nine children during the Depression and lost two, one in childhood and one in the Second World War. But Maud's life had meaning, and it touched so many others. She was devoted to her family and volunteered in her community. As a Gold Star Mother, she helped lead the cause for wounded veterans. I remember her as a loving grandmother. Maud lived long enough to see eighteen grandchildren and twenty-four great-grandchildren. Today, Amelia's descendants are numerous. I am proud to be one.

Sometimes the greatest form of justice is the truth.

Maps and Pictures

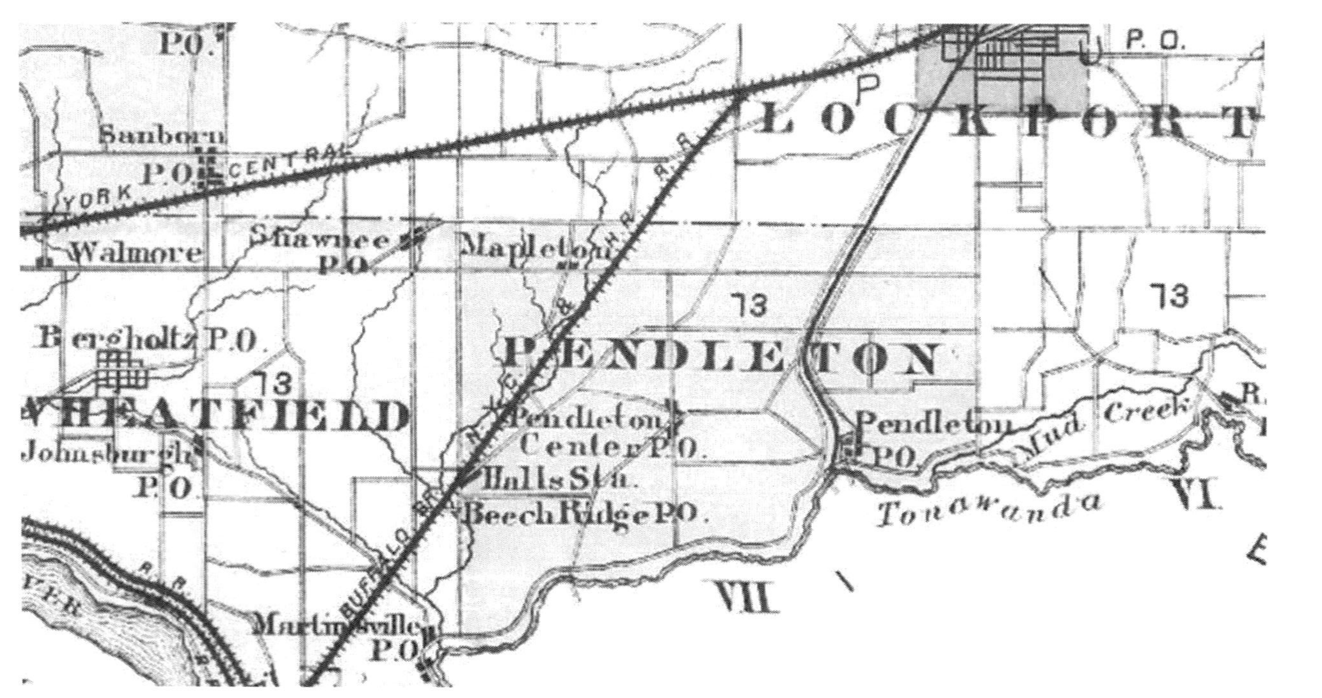

LOCKPORT
P.O.
Sanborn
P.O.
YORK CENTRAL
Walmore
Shawnee
P.O.
Mapleton
73
PENDLETON
Bergholtz P.O.
73
WHEATFIELD
Johnsburgh
P.O.
Pendleton
Center P.O.
Halls Stn.
Beech Ridge P.O.
Pendleton
P.O.
Mud Creek
Tonawanda
VI
VII
BUFFALO
Martinsville
P.O.
R.R.

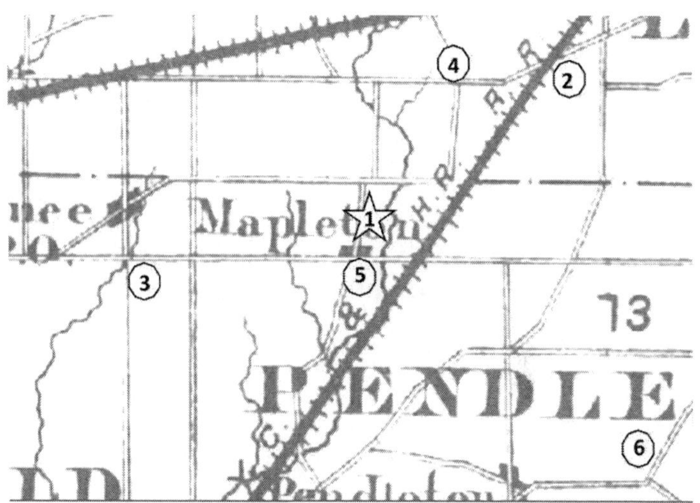

1- Tripp homestead
2- "Shawnee crossing," where Sarah's body was found.
3- Wheatfield (Shawnee) Cemetery, the site of Sarah's grave
4- where the Tripp wagon was spotted at 11:30 p.m.
5- Mapleton Presbyterian church and schoolhouse
6- Amelia's home

Map source: (both pages) The New York Public Library. (1875).

https://digitalcollections.nypl.org/

Top: Images of Sarah Mumford, left: The World, New York, NY Thursday, July 20, 1899, Page 14 www.fultonhistory.com right: *Syracuse NY Evening Herald,* July 26, 1899

Below: The only known photo of Sarah Mumford taken at the Mapleton school circa 1896, *Tonawanda News,* July 10. 1969 page 11, www.fultonhistory.com

Top: Images of Henry Tripp, (left) *The Niagara Sun*, July 25, 1899 (right) *Syracuse NY Evening Herald*, July 26, 1899

Below: photo of Lauren Tripp (left) photo of Iva Tripp (right) *Syracuse NY Evening Herald*, July 26, 1899

Acknowledgments

Extensive research would not be possible without the contributions of others. I would like to thank the many genealogical and historical societies, organizations, and individuals for their guidance and resources. Most notably:

- Niagara County Genealogical Society- *Special thanks to Jeanette Sheliga for your time and teaching.*
- Pendleton Historian, Carissa Smith
- Pendleton Town Clerk's Office- *Special thanks to Stephanie Chase for helping me find my family and never getting tired of pulling out the "Big Book."*
- Niagara County Historian's Office
- University of Rochester, Department of Rare Books, Special Collections, and Preservation
- Lenawee Historical Society (Michigan)
- Historical Society of the Tonawandas
- North Tonawanda Public Library

Finally, I am forever grateful to my sisters, Robin and Terri, for your encouragement and help. Thank you for playing history detective with me.

Sources and Notes

Sarah's Story

Chapter 1-June 8, 1899

"A Theatre Train." *The Buffalo Commercial,* January 3, 1898, Page 9 www.newspapers.com/ Accessed Feb 18, 2023

"The Geisha." *The Buffalo Commercial,* June 6, 1899, Page 14 www.newspapers.com/ Accessed Feb 18, 2023

"Sarah Mumford Kidnapped and Murdered." *The Buffalo Times,* June 18, 1899, Page 15 https://www.newspapers.com/ Accessed Feb 16, 2023

Chapter 2-April 22, 1895

Craig, O. (1889). Findings and Conclusions on an Investigation of the Rochester Orphan Asylum. United States

"The Rochester Orphan Asylum." *Rochester Democrat and Chronicle,* August 2, 1889. www.fultonhistory.com Accessed February 8, 2023

Rochester Democrat and Chronicle, Tuesday. July 8, 1890. www.fultonhistory.com Accessed February 6, 2023

"Friends of The Orphans." *Rochester Democrat and Chronicle,* Wednesday, February 10. 1892. Page 6, www.fultonhistory.com Accessed February 8, 2023

Rochester Democrat and Chronicle, (Rochester, New York) · Tue, Mar 12, 1895, · Page 7 www.newspapers.com/ Accessed Feb 17, 2023

"Their Generous Gifts." *Rochester Democrat and Chronicle*, Saturday, November 16, 1895. Page 11, www.fultonhistory.com Accessed February 8, 2023

Admission records Vol 9, 1893-1894 Hillside Children's Center papers, D.122, Rare Books, Special Collections, and Preservation, River Campus Libraries, University of Rochester (Sarah Mumford's Records)

Resch, Joseph, (2020) CUNY Hunter College, Benevolent Women of an Orphan Asylum: The Case of Rochester, New York www.academicworks.cuny.edu/cgi/viewcontent.cgi?article=1616&context=hc_sas_etds Accessed March 1, 2023

Crenson, Matthew A., Building the Invisible Orphanage: A Prehistory of the American Welfare System, Harvard University Press, Cambridge, MA 1998

Chapter 4-June 8, 1899

"Sarah Mumford Death Recalled." *Tonawanda News*, July 10. 1969 page 11, www.fultonhistory.com Accessed December 8, 2022

"Girl of Sixteen Ground to Death." *Rochester Democrat and Chronicle*, Saturday, June 10, 1899, Page 4 www.fultonhistory.com Accessed February 2, 2023

Chapter 6-June 9, 1899

"A Young Girl Killed." *The Niagara Sun*, June 13, 1899, Page 5 nyshistoricnewspapers.org/ Accessed March 31, 2023

"Girl of Sixteen Ground to Death." *Rochester Democrat and Chronicle*, Saturday, June 10, 1899, Page 4

"Laid Down on Track" *The Standard Union* (Brooklyn, New York) June 10, 1899, Page 13 www.newspapers.com/ Accessed May 12, 2023

"Say It Was Suicide." *The Buffalo Times*, June 10, 1899, Page 9 www.newspapers.com/ Accessed May 12, 2023

"Killed by a Train." *The Buffalo News* June 9, 1899, Page 16 www.newspapers.com/ Accessed May 14, 2023

"Accuse the Tripp's of Murder." *The Niagara Democrat,* July 21, 1899, Page 3 nyshistoricnewspapers.org/ Accessed March 31, 2023

"Funeral of H. L. Cleveland." *Buffalo Evening News,* April 18, 1900, www.fultonhistory.com Accessed February 6, 2023

"Young Girl's Awful Death." *Rochester Democrat and Chronicle,* May 1, 1899, Page 4 www.newspapers.com/ Accessed May 14, 2023

"Young Girl's Awful Death." *Hornellsville Weekly Tribune,* May 7, 1899, www.fultonhistory.com Accessed February 6, 2023

Chapter 8-June 11, 1899

"Was it Suicide?" *The Auburn Bulletin,* June 9, 1899, www.fultonhistory.com Accessed March 4, 2023

"Suicide Suspected." *The Buffalo Commercial,* June 9, 1899, Page 9 www.newspapers.com/ Accessed May 12, 2023

"Mapleton Excited: Suspicion That a Servant Was Victim of Foul Play." *The Buffalo Review,* June 16, 1899, Page 5 www.newspapers.com/ Accessed Feb 17, 2023

"Lockport, Niagara, June 8, 1899, Sarah Mumford," *New York, U.S. Death Index,* 1852-1956, Ancestry.com 2017

"Pendleton, NY, 1875" *U.S. Indexed County Land Ownership Maps,* Ancestry.com 2010

Pool, William editor, History of Wheatfield, New York From Landmarks of Niagara County, New York D. Mason & Co. Publishers, Syracuse, NY 1897

"Pendleton, Niagara, NY" *1900 United States Federal Census,* Ancestry.com 2010

"Tripps in Lockport Jail." *Buffalo Evening News,* July 20, 1899, Page 8 www.fultonhistory.com Accessed February 6, 2023 (Conversation with Bender)

"Sarah Mumford Kidnapped and Murdered." *The Buffalo Times,* June 18, 1899, Page 15

"Tombstone as Mysterious as Sarah Mumford Death." *Tonawanda News,* June 3, 1969, Page 14 www.fultonhistory.com Accessed February 2, 2023

"The Past is Remembered Only by a Few Words on Weathered Stones." *The Niagara Falls Gazette,* July 23, 1972, Page 4 www.fultonhistory.com Accessed February 2, 2023

Chapter 10-June 15, 1899

"Session Days Are Numbered." *Niagara Falls Gazette,* March 23, 1899, Page 1, nyshistoricnewspapers.org/ Accessed July 14, 2023

"Board of Supervisors." *Elmira Daily Gazette and Free Press,* December 6, 1899, www.fultonhistory.com Accessed March 13, 2023

"Cambria, Niagara, NY" *1900 United States Federal Census,* Ancestry.com 2010

"Accuse the Tripp's of Murder." *The Niagara Democrat,* July 21, 1899, Page 3

"Sarah Mumford Kidnapped and Murdered." *The Buffalo Times,* June 18, 1899, Page 15

"Mumford Inquest." *The Niagara Sun,* June 20, 1899, Page 7 nyshistoricnewspapers.org/ Accessed July 14, 2023

Chapter 12-June 16, 1899

Doyle, Arthur Conan, 1859-1930. *The Complete Sherlock Holmes.* Doubleday & Co., Garden City, NY 1930. "A Scandal in Bohemia" 1891, "The Sign of Four" 1890

"Murder is Suspected." *Buffalo Evening News,* June 15, 1899, Page 21 www.newspapers.com/ Accessed Feb 17, 2023

"Sensational Story." *The Niagara Democrat,* June 16, 1899, Page 1" nyshistoricnewspapers.org/ Accessed March 31, 2023

"Demand for Justice." *The Buffalo Times,* June 16, 1899, Page 7 www.newspapers.com/ Accessed Feb 19, 2023

The Poughkeepsie Evening Enterprise, June 16, 1899, www.fultonhistory.com Accessed March 13, 2023

"Hope For Results." *The Buffalo Times,* June 20, 1899, Page 7 www.newspapers.com/ Accessed May 12, 2023

"Sarah Mumford's Fate: The Mystery Surrounding Her Death Interests Tonawanda Residents." *The Buffalo Times,* June 25, 1899, Page 15" www.newspapers.com/ Accessed May 12, 2023

Biography and Portrait Encyclopedia of Niagara County, New York, Gresham Publishing Company, Philadelphia PA, 1892

"Coroner Cleveland Is again his wonted happy self. What possibly accounts for It is that "cases" are decidedly plentiful these days." *The Buffalo Courier,* July 1. 1894, page 23 www.fultonhistory.com Accessed February 5, 2023

"School Exhibition in District No. 12 in Town of Porter." *Lockport Daily Journal* March 20, 1877, www.fultonhistory.com Accessed February 6, 2023

"An Investigation Has Been Started." *The Buffalo Times,* June 17, 1899, Page 7 www.newspapers.com/ Accessed Feb 19, 2023

"Mumford Inquest." *The Niagara Sun,* June 20, 1899, Page 7

Chapter 14-June 17, 1899

"Sarah Mumford Kidnapped and Murdered." *Buffalo Times,* June 18, 1899, Page 15

McCrery, Nigel, Silent Witnesses: The Story of Forensic Science, Random House, London 2014

"A Johnson Creek Episode." *Lockport Daily Journal,* July 14, 1894, page 5 nyshistoricnewspapers.org/ Accessed April 1, 2023

Chapter 16-June 22, 1899

Adena Barnette. Patronage and Populism: The Politics of the Gilded Age. 2016. Retrieved from the Digital Public Library of America, https://production.dp.la/primary-source-sets/patronage-and-populism-the-politics-of-the-gilded-age. Accessed July 27, 2023

"Fire Fiend's Work" *Lockport Daily Sun,* October 12, 1892, page 4 nyshistoricnewspapers.org/ Accessed April 1, 2023

"Cleveland, Carnall" *Lockport Daily Sun,* April 17, 1893, page 4 nyshistoricnewspapers.org/ Accessed April 1, 2023

"Admission was Denied" *The Buffalo Times,* June 23, 1899, Page 7 www.newspapers.com/ Accessed May 12, 2023

"Mumford Inquest." *The Niagara Sun,* June 23, 1899, Page 8 nyshistoricnewspapers.org/ Accessed July 14, 2023

"Foully Dealt With" *The Buffalo Times,* June 23, 1899, Page 5 www.newspapers.com/ Accessed Feb 19, 2023

"Only First Steps So Far Taken" *The Buffalo Times,* June 24, 1899, Page 7 www.newspapers.com/ Accessed May 12, 2023

"Accuse the Tripp's of Murder" *The Niagara Democrat,* July 21, 1899, Page 3

"Family Held for Murder of Girl" *The World,* July 20, 1899, Page 14 www.fultonhistory.com Accessed February 2, 2023

"County News Mapleton Station" *Lockport Daily Journal,* October 5, 1897, Page 3, www.fultonhistory.com Accessed March 4, 2023

The Adrian Daily Telegram, Feb. 21, 1896, Lenawee Historical Society Accessed May 20, 2023

"Pendleton" *The Niagara Sun,* July 11, 1899, Page.7 nyshistoricnewspapers.org/ Accessed July 14, 2023

"Made Doubly Sure" *The Niagara Sun,* June 27, 1899, Page.1 nyshistoricnewspapers.org/ Accessed July 14, 2023

Chapter 18-June 29, 1899

"Weaving a Web." *The Niagara Sun,* June 27, 1899, Page 5 nyshistoricnewspapers.org/ Accessed July 14, 2023

"The Drought Serious" *The Niagara Sun,* June 27, 1899, Page 1 nyshistoricnewspapers.org/ Accessed July 14, 2023

"Accuse the Tripp's of Murder" The Niagara Democrat, July 21, 1899, Page 3

"Sarah's Remains Lay in Shadow" *The Buffalo Times,* June 19, 1899, Page 7 www.newspapers.com/ Accessed May 12, 2023

"Sensational Developments" *The Buffalo Times,* July 3, 1899, Page 7 www.newspapers.com/ Accessed May 12, 2023

"Tripps in Lockport Jail" *Buffalo Evening News,* July 20, 1899, Page 8

"Family Held for Murder of Girl" *The World,* July 20, 1899, Page 14

Chapter 20-July 3, 1899

"Startling Statements" *The Buffalo Times,* July 2, 1899, Page 19 www.newspapers.com/ Accessed May 12, 2023

"Adjourned again." *The Niagara Sun,* July 4, 1899, Page 7 nyshistoricnewspapers.org/ Accessed March 31, 2023

Chapter 22-July 6, 1899

"Again Adjourned." *The Niagara Sun,* July 6, 1899, Page 7 nyshistoricnewspapers.org/ Accessed March 31, 2023

"Good But Not Enough" *The Buffalo Times,* July 6, 1899, Page 1www.newspapers.com/ Accessed Feb 19, 2023

"Still Investigating a Deep Mystery*" The Buffalo Times,* July 6, 1899, Page 1" www.newspapers.com/ Accessed Feb 19, 2023

"Two Tripps Spent Last Night in Jail, cont." *The Buffalo Times,* July 20, 1899, Page 9 www.newspapers.com/ Accessed Feb 16, 2023

Admission records Vol 10, 1891 Hillside Children's Center papers, D.122, Rare Books, Special Collections, and Preservation, River Campus Libraries, University of Rochester (Sarah Mumford's Records)

Admission records Vol 9, 1893-1894 Hillside Children's Center papers, D.122, University of Rochester

"Palmyra, Wayne County, John Mumford, page 34" *1880 United States Federal Census,* Ancestry.com 2010

"Zion Episcopal Church Register, Palmyra, NY," *Episcopal Diocese of Rochester, Rochester, New York,* Volume Number: 3, Ancestry.com 2018

"Rochester Monroe, page 8, Sadie Mumford" *New York State Census 1892,* Ancestry.com 2012

Collection Overview, Industrial School of Rochester records, Rare Books, Special Collections, and Preservation, River Campus Libraries, University of Rochester rbscp.lib.rochester.edu/finding-aids/D103 Accessed June 22, 2023

Rochester Democrat and Chronicle, October 2, 1890, · Page 5 www.newspapers.com Accessed on Jun 26, 2023

"Police Report" *Rochester Democrat and Chronicle*, June 20. 1893 www.fultonhistory.com Accessed March 15, 2023

"Police Report" *Rochester Democrat and Chronicle*, December 26, 1894, www.fultonhistory.com Accessed May 26, 2023

"They Find Homes for Children" *The Buffalo Evening News*, March 14, 1894, Page 21 nyshistoricnewspapers.org/ Accessed May 31, 2023

The Johnstown Daily Republic, March 22, 1897, Page 3 nyshistoricnewspapers.org/ Accessed May 31, 2023

"A startling Charge" *The Watertown Reunion*, April 21, 1897, Page 4 nyshistoricnewspapers.org/ Accessed May 31, 2023

"Wilson" *Lockport Daily Journal*, April 20, 1897, Page 8 nyshistoricnewspapers.org/ Accessed May 31, 2023

"Herkimer Orphans" *The Utica Observer*, March 22, 1899, Page 3 nyshistoricnewspapers.org/ Accessed May 31, 2023

"About Children's Homes *Rochester Democrat and Chronicle*, · Fri, February 9, 1883" www.newspapers.com Accessed on Jun 26, 2023

"Dependent Children Subject of Traffic" *Rochester Democrat and Chronicle*, January 26, 1898, Page 10 www.newspapers.com Accessed on July 30, 2023

"Children Kept from Mother" *The World*, January 25, 1898, Page 10 www.newspapers.com Accessed on July 30, 2023

"Maybee Arrested" *Rochester Democrat and Chronicle*, February 4, 1898, Page 1 www.newspapers.com Accessed on July 30, 2023

"A Minister Arraigned" *Rochester Democrat and Chronicle*, March 3, 1898, Page 7 www.newspapers.com Accessed on July 30, 2023

"State Charitable Work" *The Brooklyn Daily Eagle,* May 29, 1898, Page 33 www.newspapers.com Accessed on July 30, 2023

Chapter 24-July 10, 1899

"Accuse the Tripp's of Murder" *The Niagara Democrat,* July 21, 1899, Page 3

"Again adjourned" *The Niagara Sun,* July 11, 1899, Page 6 nyshistoricnewspapers.org/ Accessed April 1, 2023

"Rochester, Monroe, Cora Mumford, page 10" *1900 United States Federal Census,* Ancestry.com 2010

"Fierce Row in The Bamber Block" *Rochester Democrat and Chronicle,* November 30, 1900, Page 10 www.newspapers.com Accessed on Jun 26, 2023

"Girl Will Live" *Rochester Democrat and Chronicle,* December 1, 1900, Page 16 www.newspapers.com Accessed on Jun 26, 2023

"Too Ill to Appear in Court" *Rochester Democrat and Chronicle,* December 8, 1900, Page 12 www.newspapers.com Accessed on Jun 26, 2023

"Two Prominent Hospital Cases" *Rochester Democrat and Chronicle,* January 7, 1901, Page 7 www.newspapers.com Accessed on Jun 26, 2023

"Recalls Thanksgiving night Row in Bamber Block" *Rochester Democrat and Chronicle,* January 4, 1901, Page 10 www.newspapers.com Accessed on Jun 26, 2023

"Kittie Mumford Leaves the Hospital" *Rochester Democrat and Chronicle,* January 15, 1901, Page 11 www.newspapers.com Accessed on Jun 26, 2023

"Injured by Fall" *Rochester Democrat and Chronicle,* March 8, 1895, Page 8 www.newspapers.com Accessed on Jun 28, 2023

"Weller, Eugenie" *Rochester Democrat and Chronicle*, March 20, 1919, Page 18 www.newspapers.com Accessed on Jun 26, 2023

"Allen, Cora" *Rochester Democrat and Chronicle*, January 23, 1922, Page 19 www.newspapers.com Accessed on Jun 26, 2023

"Mrs. Cora Allen" *The Wayne County Journal,* January 26, 1922, Page 4 nyshistoricnewspapers.org/ Accessed June 25, 2023

"Hartley, Catherine" *Rochester Democrat and Chronicle*, April 26, 1947, Page 28 www.newspapers.com Accessed on Jun 26, 2023

Chapter 26-July 13, 1899

"Investigating Mumford Case" *The Buffalo News*, July 14, 1899, Fri · Page 7 www.newspapers.com/ Accessed May 14, 2023

"Still Dragging Its Weary Way Along" *The Buffalo Times,* July 14, 1899, Page 7 www.newspapers.com/ Accessed May 12, 2023

"The Tripps at Home: How They Impressed a Representative of a Tonawanda Paper." *The Buffalo Times,* July 26, 1899, Wed · Page 7 www.newspapers.com/ Accessed May 12, 2023

"Accuse the Tripp's of Murder" *The Niagara Democrat,* July 21, 1899, Page 3

"Tripps in Lockport Jail" *Buffalo Evening News,* July 20, 1899, Page 8

"Family Held for Murder of Girl" *The World,* July 20, 1899, Page 14

Chapter 28-July 15, 1899

"Investigating Mumford Case" *Buffalo Evening News,* July 14, 1899, page 7.

"May Be Foul Play" *Rochester Democrat and Chronicle*, July 16, 1899, www.fultonhistory.com Accessed February 5, 2023

"A New Witness Found" *The Buffalo Times,* July 16, 1899, Page 15 www.newspapers.com/ Accessed May 12, 2023

"Two Tripps Spent Last Night in Jail, cont." *The Buffalo Times,* July 20, 1899, Page 9

"Pendleton, Niagara, page 3 Henry Bender" *1900 United States Federal Census,* Ancestry.com 2010

"Cambria, Niagara, page 1, Albert and Oscar Moyer" *1900 United States Federal Census,* Ancestry.com 2010

"Administers Estate of Mother, Brother" *Niagara Falls Gazette,* August 21, 1945, Page 13, nyshistoricnewspapers.org/ Accessed April 1, 2023

"Henry Bender" *U.S. World War I Draft Registration Cards 1917-18,* Ancestry.com 2006

"Mumford Murder Still a Mystery" *The Philadelphia Times,* July 21, 1899, Page 2 www.newspapers.com/ Accessed May 14, 2023

Chapter 30-July 17, 1899

"Body Will Be Exhumed" *Buffalo Evening News,* July 17, 1899, Page 6." www.newspapers.com/ Accessed Feb 17, 2023

"No Verdict Yet Reached" *The Buffalo Times,* July 19, 1899, Page 1 www.newspapers.com/ Accessed Feb 16, 2023

"Skilled Local Doctor Is Dead" *The Lockport Union-Sun,* October 31, 1918, Page 5, nyshistoricnewspapers.org/ Accessed April 1, 2023

"Dr. W.M. Pettit, Longtime Physician here..." *Lockport Union Sun and Journal,* July 8, 1929, page 12, nyshistoricnewspapers.org/ Accessed April 1, 2023

"Foul Play Suspected" *The Buffalo Courier,* February 9. 1892 page 1, www.fultonhistory.com Accessed February 8, 2023

"Catherine Culver; 's Death" *The Buffalo Courier,* February 14. 1892 page 1, www.fultonhistory.com Accessed February 8, 2023

Chapter 32-July 18, 1899

"Accuse the Tripp's of Murder" *The Niagara Democrat,* July 21, 1899, Page 3

"Latest Sensational Evidence in Investigation into Sarah Mumford's Death" *Rochester Democrat and Chronicle,* Wednesday, July 19, 1899, Page 4 www.fultonhistory.com Accessed February 2, 2023

"Sarah A. Mumford's Fate" *The Lockport Sun,* Lockport NY, Thursday, July 20, 1899. Page 7, www.fultonhistory.com Accessed February 2, 2023

"Was Mumford Girl Murdered?" *The Buffalo Courier,* Wednesday, July 19. 1899 page 1, www.fultonhistory.com Accessed February 8, 2023

"Murder Suspected" *Niagara Falls Gazette,* July 19, 1899, Page 1, nyshistoricnewspapers.org/ Accessed April 1, 2023

Chapter 34-July 19, 1899

"Two Tripps Spent Last Night in Jail, cont." *The Buffalo Times,* July 20, 1899, Page 9

"Awful Deed is Charged" *Rochester Democrat and Chronicle,* Thursday, July 20, 1899, www.fultonhistory.com Accessed February 5, 2023

"A Girl's Death" *The Buffalo Courier,* July 20. 1899 page 3 www.newspapers.com/ Accessed May 4, 2022

"Three Persons Held Responsible for The Girls Death" *The Buffalo Evening Times* July 19, 1899, Page 1 www.newspapers.com/ Accessed Feb 16, 2023

"Iva Is Independent and Thankless for Bail" *The Buffalo Enquirer,* July 21, 1899, Page 9 www.newspapers.com/ Accessed May 14, 2023

"About the Tripps" *The Niagara Sun,* July 21, 1899, Page 8 nyshistoricnewspapers.org/ Accessed March 31, 2023

"Pendleton, Niagara County..." *The Buffalo Courier*, July 21, 1899, page 4 www.fultonhistory.com Accessed February 2, 2023

"Tripps in Lockport Jail" *Buffalo Evening News* July 20, 1899, Page 8

Chapter 36-July 20, 1899

"Two Tripps Spent Last Night in Jail" *The Buffalo Times*, July 20, 1899, Page 1 www.newspapers.com/ Accessed Feb 19, 2023

"Tripps are now released on Bail" *Buffalo Evening News*, July 21, 1899, Page 7 www.fultonhistory.com Accessed February 2, 2023

"Tripps Secure Bail" *Niagara Falls Gazette*, July 22, 1899, Page 1, nyshistoricnewspapers.org/ Accessed April 1, 2023

"Gave a mortgage" *The Niagara Sun*, July 25, 1899, Page 5 nyshistoricnewspapers.org/ Accessed March 31, 2023

"Mystery Surrounds Death of Sarah Mumford" *Syracuse NY Evening Herald*, July 26, 1899, www.fultonhistory.com Accessed March 13, 2023

"Last Evening at Lockport..." *Rochester Democrat and Chronicle*, July 21, 1899, Page 4 www.newspapers.com/ Accessed May 14, 2023

McCrery, Nigel, Silent Witnesses: The Story of Forensic Science, Random House, London 2014

"The Tripps at Home: How They Impressed a Representative of a Tonawanda Paper." *The Buffalo Times*, July 16, 1899, Page 7

"Tripps all out." *The Niagara Sun*, July 25, 1899, Page 5 nyshistoricnewspapers.org/ Accessed March 31, 2023

Chapter 38-July 26, 1899

"Tripps at Home" *The Buffalo Times*, July 23, 1899, Page 11 www.newspapers.com/ Accessed Feb 19, 2023

"The Tripps at Home: How They Impressed...." *The Buffalo Times,* July 26, 1899, Page 7

"Whole Family Held for Crime" *The New York Press,* July 27, 1899, www.fultonhistory.com Accessed February 8, 2023

"Mystery in The Death of This Pretty Girl" *The Philadelphia Times,* July 19, 1899, Page 1 www.newspapers.com/ Accessed May 14, 2023

"Held for Murder of His Pretty Ward" *The Philadelphia Times,* July 20, 1899, Page 1 www.newspapers.com/ Accessed Feb 16, 2023

"Family Held for Murder of Girl" *The World,* July 20, 1899, Page 14

"Charged with Murder" *The Wheeling Intelligencer,* July 20. 1899. Page 1 www.fultonhistory.com Accessed February 2, 2023

"Did the Family Kill Her?" *Niagara Falls Gazette,* July 26, 1899, Page 2, nyshistoricnewspapers.org/ Accessed March 31, 2023

"Mystery Surrounds Death of Sarah Mumford" *Syracuse NY Evening Herald,* July 26, 1899

"Assaulted old man" *Lockport Daily Journal,* April 7. 1898 page 5 www.fultonhistory.com Accessed March 4, 2023

"An Error Corrected" *Lockport Daily Journal,* April 16, 1898, page 8 www.fultonhistory.com Accessed March 4, 2023

"Indictments" *Lockport Daily Journal,* April 22, 1898, Page 5 www.fultonhistory.com Accessed March 4, 2023

Lockport Daily Journal, April 23, 1898, page 5 www.fultonhistory.com Accessed March 4, 2023

"Tripp's examination" *The Buffalo Express,* July 29, 1899. www.fultonhistory.com Accessed March 4, 2023

"The postponement of the preliminary examination" *The Buffalo Commercial,* July 31, 1899, Monday Page 7 www.newspapers.com/ Accessed May 14, 2023

Chapter 40-August 11, 1899

"Accuse the Tripp's of Murder" *The Niagara Democrat,* July 21, 1899, Page 3

The Buffalo Times, August 11, 1899, Page 7 www.newspapers.com/ Accessed May 4, 2023

New York State Birth Record, Town of Clarence, Niagara County, Margret Susan Tripp, September 28, 1897

Record of Death, Town of Clarence, Erie County, State of New York, Susan Margret Tripp, November 24, 1897

Chapter 42-August 18, 1899

"Dead Before Train Hit Her" *Buffalo Evening News*, August 18, 1899, Page 4 www.newspapers.com/ Accessed May 4, 2022

"Tripp Murder Case" *Buffalo Courier,* August 19, 1899, Page 1 www.fultonhistory.com Accessed February 2, 2023

"She Was Not Killed by Locomotive" *The Buffalo Review,* August 19, 1899, Page 8www.fultonhistory.com Accessed February 2, 2023

"Tripp Case Up Again" *The Buffalo Enquirer,* August 19, 1899, Page 6 www.newspapers.com/ Accessed May 12, 2023

"Mumford Case" *The Niagara Sun,* August 22, 1899, Page 7 nyshistoricnewspapers.org/ Accessed March 31, 2023

Chapter 44-September 11, 1899

"Postponement*" Buffalo Evening News*, September 4. 1899 page 7" www.fultonhistory.com Accessed March 13, 2023

"Calendar for the Supreme Court September 99" *The Niagara Sun,* September 8, 1899, Page 8 nyshistoricnewspapers.org/ Accessed March 31, 2023

Buffalo Evening News, September 10, 1899, Page 3 www.newspapers.com/ Accessed Feb 17, 2023

Chapter 46-September 28, 1899

"Tripps are Clear of Murder Charge" *The Buffalo Enquirer,* September 28, 1899, Page 1 www.newspapers.com/ Accessed May 12, 2023

"Tripps Go Free" *The Buffalo Review,* September 29, 1899, Page 5 www.fultonhistory.com Accessed February 2, 2023

Buffalo Courier September 29, 1899, Page 2 www.newspapers.com/ Accessed May 4, 2022

"The Tripp Case" *Niagara Falls Gazette,* October 3, 1899, Page 1, nyshistoricnewspapers.org/ Accessed April 1, 2023

"No Indictment against the Tripps" *The Buffalo Times,* September 28, 1899, Page 1 www.newspapers.com/ Accessed May 4, 2023

"Many Speculations Regarding the Mumford Case-Was It Murder?" *The Buffalo News,* July 23, 1899, Page 16 www.newspapers.com/ Accessed May 14, 2023

Chapter 48-October 26, 1899

Buffalo Evening News, October 24, 1899, www.fultonhistory.com Accessed March 13, 2023

Chapter 49- March 6, 1900

"Expert Juggling" *The Niagara Sun,* January 5, 1900, Page 1 nyshistoricnewspapers.org/ Accessed April 1, 2023

"Illness is serious" *Niagara Falls Gazette,* February 12, 1900, Page 1, nyshistoricnewspapers.org/ Accessed April 1, 2023

"Dr. Cleveland out of Misery *Buffalo Courier,* April 14, 1900, Page 2" www.fultonhistory.com Accessed February 6, 2023

"Tripp" *The Niagara Sun,* March 6, 1900, Page 8 nyshistoricnewspapers.org/ Accessed April 1, 2023

Register of Birth, Town of Pendleton, New York, Raymond Tripp, April 7, 1899

Register of Death, Town of Pendleton, New York, Raymond Tripp, March 2, 1900

The Adrian Daily Telegram, Apr.18, 1900, Lenawee Historical Society Accessed May 20, 2023

Chapter 50- 1901

"Thirteenth Victim of The Asylum Fire" *Rochester Democrat and Chronicle,* January 10, 1901. Page 9, www.fultonhistory.com Accessed February 8, 2023

"Thirty-one on the death roll" *Rochester Democrat and Chronicle,* January 11, 1901. Page 10, www.fultonhistory.com Accessed February 8, 2023

"Comments on the Fire" *Rochester Democrat and Chronicle,* January 10, 1901. Page 6, www.fultonhistory.com Accessed February 8, 2023

"Death of the Orphans" *Rochester Democrat and Chronicle,* January 24, 1901. Page 12, www.fultonhistory.com Accessed February 8, 2023

"Rev. Mr. Maybee Again" *The Utica Observer,* August 28, 1900, Page 3 nyshistoricnewspapers.org/ Accessed May 31, 2023

"Rev. Mr. Maybee Acquitted*" The Buffalo Evening News,* April 11, 1901, Page 17" nyshistoricnewspapers.org/ Accessed May 31, 2023

Chapter 52-1902

"Round the County: Mapleton" *The Lockport Journal,* March 27, 1902, www.fultonhistory.com Accessed February 2, 2023

The Adrian Daily Telegram, 1945, Mrs. Carrie Tripp (Obituary) Lenawee Historical Society Accessed May 22, 2023

Amelia's Story

I have been researching my family for more than twenty years, I limited the sources to those directly pertaining to this story.

1895 Chapter

Niagara County, NY Death Certificate, Pendleton, Rachael Knople - died 5/14/1895 at age 18 (single) from Diabetes Insipidus in Pendleton; parents were Henry & Rachel Knople of Germany; occupation was Domestic; medical attendant was J.E. Helwig; buried in Martinsville.

Dr. Helwig was the physician on record for both Rachael Knople's death and Maud's birth. He was also the coroner who investigated Amelia's death. He went on to serve honorably as a Niagara County Coroner until he died in 1944

"Amelia Knipple" Souvenir School Card, Pendleton School District # 3 (1896-1897) Pendleton Historical Society

Niagara County, NY Deed of Sale, Pendleton Lot 69 (1864) Charle Knipple

"Pendleton, Niagara, page 14, Henry Knipple," *New York State Census 1892,* Ancestry.com 2012

National Archives Civil War Veterans and Pension Records, Frederick Knobel

1899 Chapters

National Archives Civil War Veterans and Pension Records, Frederick Knobel

"Frederick Knobel," *US National Home for Disabled Volunteer Soldiers, 1866-1938,* Ancestry.com 2007

Jones, Jonathan "Civil War Veterans, and Opiate Addiction," C-SPAN, October 22, 2020, www.c-span.org/video/?477833-1/civil-war-veterans-opiate-addiction Viewed May 2022 *An estimated 400,000 other Civil War vets in our country's first opiate epidemic.*

"Horrors of County Poorhouses" *The Lockport Sun,* December 14, 1883, www.fultonhistory.com Accessed February 6, 2023

"Pendleton, Niagara, Henry Knibel page 43" *1865 New York State Census*, ancestry.com 2014

Niagara County, NY, Petition for U.S. Citizenship, (1867) Frederick Knobel, (1869) Charles Knoble

Niagara County, NY Deed of Sale, Pendleton Lot 69, Charle Knipple, 1864

Register of Birth, Town of Pendleton, New York, Maud Knople, July 25, 1899

"Pendleton, Niagara, p.6, Henry Knippel" *1900 United States Federal Census*, Ancestry.com 2010

"Erie County, Fred Knoble, 1885,1886,1890" *New York U.S. Governors Registers of Commitments to Prisons, 1842-1908,* Ancestry.com 2014

I found most of the information about Uncle Fritz in Frederick Knople's lengthy pension file. I know Aunt Katherine stayed connected with the family because Henry Knople stated so in an affidavit to help Katherine collect her widow's pension in 1902.

"Weird story of witchcraft told in court," *The Buffalo Times,* May 9, 1913, Page 7 www.newspapers.com Accessed on May 4, 2022

"Strings of feathers tied by human hair used by cruel spooks." *Buffalo Evening News,* May 8, 1913, Page 3 www.newspapers.com Accessed on May 4, 2022

In 1913, one of Katherine Knople's neighbors accused her of being a witch and putting a curse on their daughter. The incident went to court and made the newspapers. Katherine countersued for slander and the judge ordered the neighbors to stop spreading the rumor.

1901 Chapters

Register of Birth, Town of Pendleton, New York, Mary Knople, June 9, 1901
"Pendleton Center. July 14, 1901, William Glaff and Amelia Knipple," *New York State, Marriage Index 1881-1967,* Ancestry.com 2017

1903 Chapters

Coroner's Report, Niagara County Clerk, Amelia Glaff, 1903

"North Tonawanda, October 18, 1903, Amelia Glauf," *New York State Death Index 1880-1956,* Ancestry.com, 2017

New York State Death Certificate, North Tonawanda Town Clerk, William Glauf, October 17, 1903

New York State Death Certificate, North Tonawanda Town Clerk, Marie Glauf, October 19, 1903

"Three Deaths in One Family" *Buffalo Evening News,* October 21, 1903, Page 19 www.newspapers.com/ Accessed May 4, 2022

"Coroner is Investigating," *The Tonawanda Evening News,* October 20, 1903, page 1, accessed at North Tonawanda Public Library

"Blood Poisoning," *The Tonawanda Evening*, October 21, 1903, page 1, accessed at North Tonawanda Public Library

"Annual Meeting of Home for Friendless" *The Lockport Journal,* October 13, 1904, Page 7, nyshistoricnewspapers.org/ Accessed April 1, 2023

"Reports for Year: Statements by Officers of Home for Friendless" *The Lockport Journal* October 16, 1903, Page 1, nyshistoricnewspapers.org/ Accessed April 1, 2023

"Hurt at Higginsville" *Syracuse Journal,* June 1, 1904, page 8, www.fultonhistory.com Accessed February 4, 2022

The Buffalo Commercial, Monday, June 6, 1904, Page 8 www.newspapers.com/ Accessed May 4, 2022

Buffalo Evening News, June 6, 1904, www.newspapers.com/ Accessed May 4, 2022

New York State Death Certificate, City of Oneida Clerk, William H. Glawf, June 4, 1904

"North Tonawanda, Niagara, page 2, Charles Graff" *1900 United States Federal Census,* Ancestry.com 2010

Register of Death, Town of Pendleton, New York, Henry Knoeple, November 11, 1903

"Henry Knople" *Tonawanda News,* November 11, 1903, accessed at North Tonawanda Public Library

"Fredericka Knople" *Tonawanda News,* December 1905 accessed at North Tonawanda Public Library

"North Tonawanda, Niagara p.10, Charles Graf," *New York State census, 1905,* Ancestry.com 2014

About the Author

Michelle Graff, author of *Hidden: The Unsolved Mystery of Sarah Mumford,* found the perfect convergence of her diverse interests in her third book.

As a child, she dreamed of being an investigative journalist, but her sense of social justice led her to a career in child welfare. After twenty-five years of advocating for children and families, she put her love of research and writing to good use. She published her first book, *The Compassion Fatigued Organization,* and founded a business to help organizations and professionals combat secondary trauma.

As an amateur genealogist, she has been researching her family history for almost three decades.

Finally, as a fan of books and puzzles, she is drawn to mystery and true crime novels. Like so many true crime lovers, she longed to solve a real-life mystery.

Fellow fans of history, genealogy, research, puzzles, true crime, mystery, social justice, and child advocacy can contact her at resiliencyonline.com.

Made in the USA
Middletown, DE
22 March 2024

51924212R00146